Ted Thomas
Author, Publisher

Ted Thomas is a Florida based publisher and author. His negotiation articles are syndicated in newspapers and magazines nationwide.

Eighteen California legal newspapers carry negotiation articles which are written from the perspective of the average man. *Creative Real Estate* magazine features negotiating tips in monthly articles.

Ted Thomas is a publisher and author of 11 books. His guidebooks on Real Estate have sold in four countries of the world.

His best selling Video Home Study Course, SMART MONEY RETIRES RICH, is considered the bench mark standard for the Tax Lien industry.

Thomas' other publications have been carried in book stores and libraries for many years. Although Thomas is best known for his comprehensive Home Study Program UP FOR GRABS - MILLIONS IN FORECLOSURE REAL ESTATE, a National best seller, Thomas conducts live tours of tax lien sales in most states and conducts negotiation seminars on a regular schedule.

After watching his parents work hard their whole lives and die almost broke, Thomas decided it was time to dedicate his time to finding an investment strategy that would help senior citizens, as well as young people, avoid the humiliation of not having enough money. In the two years of researching and traveling, Ted visited thirty states and hundreds of counties, he interviewed dozens of government officers and venture capitalists. From that effort, emerged the most comprehensive program for low risk and high yield returns available in the U.S.A. These discoveries are almost hidden government programs that yield up to 25% interest. Surprisingly, these government-sponsored programs have been almost secret for decades.

D0884832

ACKNOWLEDGEMENT

No book is written just by the author. Grateful acknowledgement goes to all those who helped and contributed along the way.

Thanks to Pennye Nelson and Guy Richardson for their editorial and design.

Attorney at Law, Joel Moskowitz for his contributions and materials on toxic hazards.

Thanks to Attorney at Law, John Beck for his advice and pioneering ideas on Tax Deed Certificate hidden market.

A special hand clasp across the miles to author Dr. Donald Moine for his editorial insight as to what the reader is looking for and how to present the information.

This guidebook would have never reached your hands without the help and assistance of all the unnamed, diligent county - public employees and officials who went out of their way to assist, educate and guide this endeavor to its completion.

HOW TO MAKE YOUR
PERSONAL FORTUNE
WITH GOVERNMENT MONEY™

DIRECTORY Tax Deed Certificates

TED THOMAS

DISCLAIMER

This publication is intended to provide accurate and authoritative information with regard to the subject matter covered. It is offered with the understanding that neither the publisher, nor the author is engaged in rendering legal, accounting or professional services. If legal advise, or expert assistance is required, the services of a competent professional person should be retained.

Every effort has been made to reflect accurate information. However, this is a dynamic field of endeavor in which new laws are enacted, old laws revised and/or interpreted on a continuing basis. Readers are advised to proceed with caution before implementing the strategies contained herein and consult with appropriate professional advisors prior to committing time and financial resources as a result of the material contained in this book or in the seminar from which it was obtained. It is for instructional purpose only.

All Rights Reserved

Published in the United States of America.

Table of Contents

THIS PAGE INTENTIONALLY LEFT BLANK FOR NOTES

HOW TO USE THIS DIRECTORY

In order to use this directory in the most effective manner, I suggest you copy the following questions and have them ready while you are telephoning the Treasurer's office. If you prefer to write for the information, simply write the appropriate person who is listed, or telephone and request from the clerk the person's name to whom you should direct your written questions.

WHAT YOU'LL WANT TO KNOW BEFORE YOU LEAVE HOME
TAX DEED QUESTIONS

1. Where and when will the sale be held. Specifically, street address, building, floor, room number.

2. Where will the public notice be posted? What newspaper - get telephone number and cost.

3. Will the sale be more than one day?

4. How many sales does the County Treasurer or Tax Collector plan this year?

5. Will the sale be advertised in more than one newspaper? Or can I get a list from the county?

6. Can I register by mail?

7. Will the auctioneer use rotational biding or some other method?

8. How much money will I need? Are all the certificates the same?

9. What method of payment is required? All cash? Cashier's check? Personal checks?

10. Will I get my certificate right away?

11. Is it possible to buy via the U. S. mail?

12. Will the auctioneer sell all the certificates? If not, how do I buy the remaining certificates if I want them?

13. What happens if the property tax is left unpaid – in other words, what happens if the property owner doesn't pay – who does the foreclosure – what will it cost?

14. Can I be put on the mailing list to get future notices of publications?

15. Is the state law (statutes) available in a condensed version? Can you mail or fax it to me?

Alaska

ALASKA

Number of Counties: 11

ANCHORAGE

Phone: (907) 343-6925
Delinquent Property Tax Division
P.O. Box 196650
Anchorage, AK 99519-0650
Ellen Braden

FAIRBANKS NORTH STAR BOROUGH

Phone: (907) 459-1444
Delinquent Property Tax Division
P.O. Box 71267
Fairbanks, AK 99707
Renee VanNort

JUNEAU

Phone: (907) 586-5218
Delinquent Property Tax Division
155 S. Seward St.
Juneau, AK 99801
Carol Meisner

KENAI PENINSULA

Phone: (907) 262-4441
Delinquent Property Tax Division
P.O. Box 3040
Soldotna, AK 99669
Larry Simmons

BRISTOL BAY

Phone: (907) 246-4224
Delinquent Property Tax Division
P.O. Box 189
Naknek, AK 99633
John McCracken

HAINES

Phone: (907) 766-2711
Delinquent Property Tax Division
P.O. Box 1209
Haines, AK 99827
Connie Staska

KETCHIKAN GATEWAY

Phone: (907) 228-6620
Delinquent Property Tax Division
344 Front St.
Ketchikan, AK 99901
Alvin Hall

KODIAK ISLAND

Phone (907) 486-9322
Delinquent Property Tax Division
710 Mill Bay Road
Kodiak, AK 99615
Karlton Short

MATANUSKA SUSTINA

Phone: (907) 745-9610
Delinquent Property Tax Division
350 E. Dahia Ave.
Palmer, AK 99645
Pam Strahan

NORTH SLOPE

Phone: (907) 852-2875
Delinquent Property Tax Division
P.O. Box 69
Barrow, AK 99723
Donna Miller

SITKA

Phone: (907) 747-1820
Delinquent Property Tax Division
100 Lincoln St.
Sitka, AK 99835
Rick Anderson

© PERSONAL FORTUNE Jones & Trevor Marketing

California

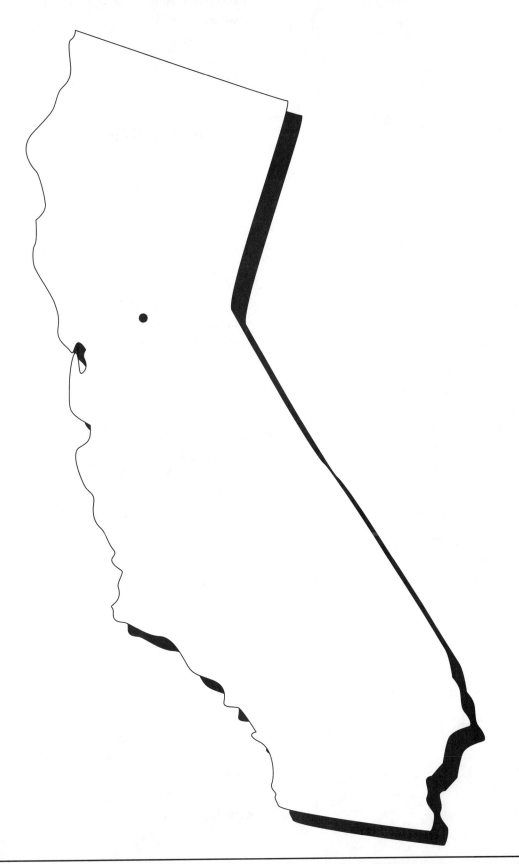

CALIFORNIA

Number of Counties: 56

ALAMEDA

Phone: (510) 272-6800
Alameda County Administration Bldg.
1221 Oak St.
Delinquent Property Tax Division
Oakland, CA 94612
Donald R. White

AMADOR

Phone: (209) 223-6364
Delinquent Property Tax Division
108 Court St.
500 Argonaut Lane
Jackson, CA 95642
Micahel E. Ryan

BUTTE

Phone: (916) 538-7539
Delinquent Property Tax Division
25 County Center Dr.
Oroville, CA 95965
Richard Puelicher

CALAVERAS

Phone: (209) 754-6350
Government Center
891 Mountain Ranch Rd.
San Andreas, CA 95249-9709
JoAnn Inks

CONTRA COSTA

Phone: (510) 646-4122
Delinquent Property Tax Division
651 Pine St.
P.O. Box 631
Martinez, CA 94553
Alfred Lomeli

EL DORADO

Phone: (916) 621-5800
P.O. Box 678002
Placerville, CA 95667
C.L. Raffety

FRESNO

Phone: (209) 488-3482
Delinquent Property Tax Division
2281 Tulare St.
Hall of Records, Rm 105
Fresno, CA 93721
Gary Peterson

HUMBOLDT

Phone: (707) 445-7331
825 5th St., Room 125
Eureka, CA 95501
Stephen Strawn

IMPERIAL

Phone: (619) 339-4301
Delinquent Property Tax Division
940 W. Main
El Centro, CA 92243
Donna Yarnell

KERN

Phone: (805) 861-2601
Delinquent Property Tax Division
1115 Truxtun Ave.
Bakersfield, CA 93301
Phillip Franey

KINGS

Phone: (209) 582-3211 ext. 2480
King County Tax Collector
1400 W. Lacey Blvd. Bldg. 7
Hanford, CA 93230
Vee-Jay Brann
Attn: Laurie

LAKE

Phone: (707) 263-2367
Delinquent Property Tax Division
255 N. Forbes
Lakeport, CA 95453

LASSEN

Phone: (916) 251-8221
220 S. Lassen
Susanville, CA 96130
Beatrice Price

LOS ANGELES

Phone: (213) 974-2045
Delinquent Property Tax Division
225 North Hill
Los Angeles, CA 90012
Larry J. Monteilh

MADERA

Phone: (209) 675-7713
Delinquent Property Tax Division
209 W. Yosemite Ave.
Madera, CA 93637
Tracy Kennedy-Desmond

MARIN

Phone: (415) 499-6133
Marin County Tax Collector
P.O. Box 4220
Delinquent Property Tax Division
San Rafael, CA 94913
Michael Smith

MENDOCINO

Phone: (707) 463-4321
Mendocino County Tax Collector
501 Low Gap Road
Room 1060
Delinquent Property Tax Division
Ukiah, CA 95482
Tim Knudsen
Attn: Shari

MERCED

Phone: (209) 385-7592 ext.4351
2222 M. St.
Merced, CA 95340
Jabres L. Ball
Attn: Sharon

MONTEREY

Phone: (408) 647-7857
P.O. Box 891
Salinas, CA 93902-0891
Sale: January 25, 1995
Lou Solton

NAPA

Phone: (707) 253-4311
Delinquent Property Tax Division
P.O. Box 629
Napa, CA 94559-0629
Marcia Humphrey

NEVADA

Phone: (916) 265-1285
P.O. Box 128
Nevada City, CA 95959-0128
E. Christina Dabis

ORANGE

Phone: (714) 834-5701
P.O. Box 1438
Santa Ana, CA 92702
John MW Moorlach

PLACER

Phone: (916) 889-4127
137 Fulweiler Ave.
Auburn, CA 95603
Jenine Windeshausen
Attn: Karen

RIVERSIDE

Phone: (909) 275-3999 not in service
P.O. Box 12005
Riverside, CA 92502-2205
R. Wayne Watts
Attn: Donna

SACRAMENTO

Phone: (916) 440-6621
700 "H" Street, Rm 1710
Sacramento, CA 95814-1285
John Dard

SAN BENITO

Phone: (408) 636-4034
Delinquent Property Tax Division
440 5th St., Rm 107
Hollister, CA 95023
Mary Lou Andrade

SAN BERNARDINO

Phone: (909) 387-6383
Delinquent Property Tax Division
172 W. 3rd St.
San Bernardino, CA 92415
Tom O'Donnel

SAN DIEGO

Phone: (619) 531-5844
1600 Pacific Hwy, Rm 162
San Diego, CA 92101
Paul Boland

SAN FRANCISCO

Phone: (415) 554-4409
Delinquent Property Tax Division
875 Stevenson St., Rm 220
San Francisco, CA 94103
Richard Sullivan
Attn: Real Estate Division

SAN JOAQUIN

Phone: (209) 468-2133
Delinquent Property Tax Division
P.O. Box 2169
Stockton, CA 95201-2169
Thomas R. Russel
c/o Redemtion Dept.

SAN LUIS OBISPO

Phone: (805) 781-5830
Delinquent Property Tax Division
San Luis Obispo Cty. Govt. Center
Rm. 203
San Luis Obispo, CA 93408-2060
Frank L. Freitas

SAN MATEO

Phone: (415) 363-4580/4041
Delinquent Property Tax Division
2200 Broadway
Redwood City, CA 94063
Lee Buffington
Pacifican Tribune

SANTA BARBARA

Phone: (805) 568-2490
Delinquent Property Tax Division
P.O. Box 579
Santa Barbara, CA 93102-0579
Gary Freamisco
Attn: Clint Donati

SANTA CLARA

Phone: (408) 299-4777
Tax Collector
70 W. Hedding St.
San Jose, CA 95110-1767
Emma Rock

SANTA CRUZ

Phone: (408) 454-2450
Delinquent Property Tax Division
P.O. Box 1817
Santa Cruz, CA 95061-1817
Richard Bedal

SHASTA

Phone: (916) 225-5511
Delinquent Property Tax Division
P.O. Box 1805
Redding, CA 56099
Jack C. Williams

SISKIYOU

Phone: (916) 842-8340
Delinquent Property Tax Division
P.O. Box 600
Yreka, CA 96097
Susan Reather

SOLANO

Phone: (707) 421-7485
600 Texas Street
Fairfield, CA 94533
Virginia Ryan
Daily Republic

SONOMA

Phone: (707) 527-3222
P.O. Box 3879
Santa Rosa, CA 95402-3879
Donald Merz
Attn: Jane

STANISLAUS

Phone: (209) 525-6388
Delinquent Property Tax Division
P.O. Box 859
Modesto, CA 95353
Tom Watson

SUTTER

Phone: (916) 822-7117
Sutter Co. Tax Collector
P.O. Box 546
Yuba City, CA 95992
Jim Stevens

TEHAMA

Phone: (916) 527-4535
Delinquent Property Tax Division
P.O. Box 769
Red Bluff, CA 96080
Doris Forward

TULARE

Phone: (209) 733-6526
Delinquent Property Tax Division
County Civic Center, Rm 103E
Visalia, CA 93291
Gerald Fields

TUOLUMNE

Phone: (209) 533-5544
P.O. Box 3248
Sonora, CA 95370
Frank Delttodges

ALPINE

Phone: (916) 694-2286
Delinquent Property Tax Division
P.O. Box 217
Markleeville, CA 96120
Doranna Glettig

COLUSA

Phone: (916) 458-0440
Delinquent Property Tax Division
546 Jay St.
Colusa, CA 95932
Daniel Charter

DEL NORTE

Phone: (707) 464-7283
641 5th St.
Crescent City, CA 95531
Sarah Sampels

GLENN

Phone: (916) 934-6410
Delinquent Property Tax Division
P.O. Box 151
Willows, CA 95988
Joe Sites

INYO

Phone: (619) 878-0301 not in service
Delinquent Property Tax Division
P.O. Box O
Independence, CA 93526
John Treacy

MARIPOSA

Phone: (209) 966-2621
P.O. Box 36
Mariposa, CA 95338
Don Phillips

MODOC

Phone: (916) 233-6223
Tax Collector
204 S. Court Street
Alturas, CA 96101
Linda Monroe

MONO

Phone: (619) 932-5265
Delinquent Property Tax Division
P.O. Box 495
Bridgeport, CA 93517
Shirley Cranney

PLUMAS

Phone: (916) 283-6260 not in service
P.O. Box 176
Quincy, CA 95971
Barbara J. Coates

SIERRA

Phone: (916) 289-3286
Delinquent Property Tax Division
P.O. Box 376
Downieville, CA 95936
Cindy Ellsmore

TRINITY

Phone: (916) 623-1252
Delinquent Property Tax Division
P.O. Box 1297
Weaverville, CA 96093
Linda Hymas

VENTURA

Phone: (805) 654-3744
Delinquent Property Tax Division
800 S. Victoria Ave.
Ventura, CA 93009-1290
Harold S. Pittman

Delaware

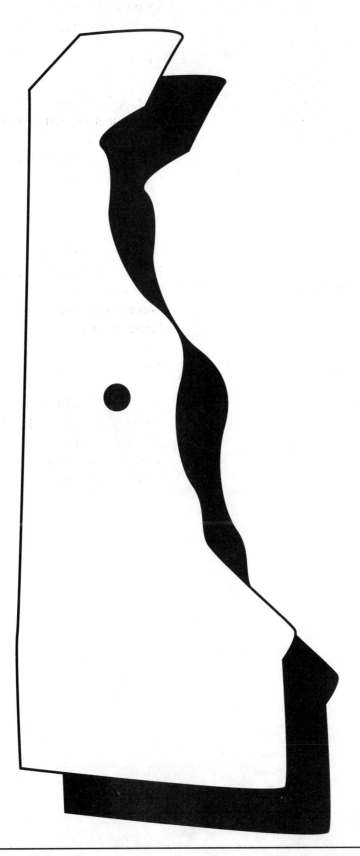

DELAWARE

Number of Counties: 3

Over 25,000 Population

KENT

Phone: (302) 736-2077
Delinquent Property Tax Division
Kent County Administration Bldg.
414 Federal St.
Dover, DE 19901
Joyce Melvin

NEW CASTLE

Phone: (302) 571-7564
Delinquent Property Tax Division
City County Building
800 French St.
Wilmington, DE 19801
Ann Elder-Nutter

SUSSEX

Phone: (302) 855-7766
P.O. Box 429
Georgetown, DE 19947
Joyce Lord

Georgia

GEORGIA

APPLING

100 Oak St.
Baxley, GA 31513-2028
(912) 367-8105
Debra S. Carter

ATKINSON

Box 98
Pearson, GA 31642
(912) 422-7381
Karen T. Bohannon

BACON

Box 432
Alma, GA 31510
(912) 632-5614
(912) 632-7422
Roger J. Taylor

BAKER

P.O. Box 450
Newton, GA 31770-0450
(912) 734-3010
Ann O. Bush

BALDWIN

Courthouse Room #3
Milledgeville, GA 31061-3399
(912) 453-4813
Cathy Freeman-Settle

BANKS

P.O. Box 40
Homer, GA 30547-0040
(706) 677-2320
Margaret Ausburn

BARROW

P.O. Box 765
Winder, GA 30680-0765
(770) 307-3106
Melinda Wall-Willliams

BARTOW

135 W. Cherokee Ave., #217A
Cartersville, GA 30120-3101
(770) 387-5111
Jack Nally

BEN HILL

P.O. Box 1393
Fitzgerald, GA 31750-1393
(912) 426-5144
Linda Faye Taylor

BERRIEN

P.O. 248
Nashville, GA 31639-0248
(912)686-7461
Lorene T. Dorminey

BIBB

P.O. Box 4724
Macon, GA 31213-0899
(912) 749-6500
Davis L. Minshew

BLECKLEY

306 S.E. Second St.
Cochran, GA 31014-1633
(912) 934-3203
Marian S. Holland

BRANTLEY

P.O. box 829
Nahunta, GA 31553-0829
(912) 462-5853
Lorna Thomas

BROOKS

Box 349
Quitman, GA 31643-0349
(912) 263-4586
Ada J. Dodd

BRYAN

Box 447
Pembroke, GA 31321—0447
(912) 653-4681
Debbie M. Newman

BULLOCH

Box 245
Statesboro, GA 30459
(912) 764-6285
James W. Deal

BURKE

Box 671
Waynesboro, GA 30830-0671
(706) 554-7880
Cynthia D. McManus

BUTTS

Box 1400
Jackson, GA 30233-1400
(770) 775-8206
Hilda K. James

CALHOUN

Box 111
Morgan, GA 31766-0111
(912) 849-2970
Mary V. Jackson

CAMDEN

P.O. Box 698
Woodbine, GA 31569-0698
(912)576-3248

CANDLER

Courthouse Square
Metter, GA 30439
(912) 685-5247
H.V. Lanier

CARROLL

423 College St., Rm. 402
Carrollton, GA 30117
(770) 830-5843
Jean . Matthews

CATOOSA

7703 Nashville St.
Ringgold, GA 30736-1799
Sandra K. Self

CHARLTON

100 Third St.
Folkston, GA 31537-3706
(912) 496-2058
"Bo" Monroe Todd

CHATHAM

P.O. Box 98237
Savannah, GA 31412-9827
(912) 652-7115
Daniel T. Powers

CHATTAHOOCHEE

Box 117
Cusseta, GA 31805-0117
(706) 989-3897
Linda W. St.John

CHATTOOGA

P.O. Box 517
Summerville, GA 30747-0517
(706) 857-0703
Hugh Don Hall

CHEROKEE

130 E. Main St., #206
Canton, GA 30114-2756
(770) 479-1953
David Fields

CLARKE

P.O. 1768
Athens, GA 30603
(706) 613-3120
Nancy B. Denson

CLAY

P.O. Box 217
Fort Gaines, GA 31751-0217
(912) 768-2915
Joyce W. Kuykendol

CLAYTON

121 S. McDonough St.
Courthouse Annex #3
Jonesboro, GA 30236-3604
Patricia Hussey

CLINCH

100 Court Square
Homerville, GA 31634-1523
(912) 487-3248
Lottie L. Bruce

COBB

100 Cherokee St.
Marietta, GA 30090-9660
(770) 528-8600
James McDuffie

COFFEE

P.O. Box 1207.
Douglas, GA 31533
(912) 384-4895

COLQUITT

P.O. Box 99
Moultrie, GA 31776
(912) 891-7410
Cindy S. Harvin

COLUMBIA

P.O. Box 56
Appling, GA 30802-0056
(706) 541-1808
Kay Allen

COOK

212 N. Hutchinson Ave.
Adel, GA 31620
(912) 896-4560
Donald E. Simmons

COWETA

P.O. Box 195
Newnan, GA 30264-0195
(77-) 254-2670
Tommy J. Ferrell

CRAWFORD

P.O. Box 634
Roberta. GA 31078-0634
Cynthia G. Davis

CRISP

Courthouse, Rm. 201`
Cordele, GA 31015-4295
(912)276-2630
Cornelia S. Adkins

DADE

P.O. Box 349
Trenton, GA 30752-0349
(706) 657-7563
Jane Moreland

DAWSON

P.O. Box 7
Dawsonville, GA 30534-0007
(706) 265-2860
Hubert D. Bailey

DECATUR

P.O. Box 246
Bainbridge, GA 31718-0246
(912) 248-3009
C.B. Hester Jr.

DEKALB

120 W. Trinity Place
Decatur, GA 30030-3221
(404) 371-8297
Tom Scott

DODGE

P.O. Box 668
Eastman, GA 31023-0668
(912) 374-22154
Dillard Skipper

DOOLY

P.O. Box 371
Vienna, GA 31092-0371
(912) 268-4212
Louise J. Bowen

DOUGHERTY

P.O. Box 1827
Albany, GA 31702-5301
(912) 431-2130
Denver Collins

DOUGLAS

P.O. Box 1177.
Douglasville, GA 30134
(770) 920-7272
Ann Jones

EARLY

Box 768
Blakely GA 31723-1811
(912) 723-4024
Jimmie H. Dunn

ECHOLS

P.O. Box 113
Statenville, GA 31648-0113
(912) 559-5253
Eleanor F. Smith

EFFINGHAM

Box 787
Springfield, GA 31329-0787
(912) 754-6071
Lisa E. Wright

ELBERT

P.O. Box 603
Elberton, GA 30635
(706) 283-2018
Mary Jean H. Ginn

EMANUEL

P.O. Box 763
Swainsboro, GA 30401-0763
(912) 237-3351
Sandra S. Wright

EVANS

P.O. Box 685
Claxton, GA 30417-0685
(912) 739-1147
Gwendolyn G. Odom

FANNIN

Box 334
Blue Ridge, GA 30513-0334
(706) 632-2645
Windell Davis

FAYETTE

P.O. Box 70
Fayetteville, GA 30214
(770) 461-3611
George Wingo

FLOYD

P.O. box 26
Rome, GA 31602-0026
(706) 291-5148
James A. Ford

FORSYTH

110 E. Main St., suite 130
Cumming, GA 30130-2463
(770) 781-2110
Bobby Gene Gilbert

FRANKLIN

P.O. Box 100
Carnesville, GA 30521
(706) 384-3455
Richard C. Holland

FULTON

141 Pryor St., S.W.
Atlanta, GA 30303
(404) 730-6602
Arthur E. Ferdinand

GILMER

P.O. Box 361
Ellijay, GA 30540
(706) 635-4762
Frank Elliott

GLASCOCK

P.O. Box 221
Gibson, GA 30810-0221
(706)598-3151
Catherine K. Kelley

GLYNN

P.O. box 1259
Brunswick, GA 31521-1259
(912) 267-5680
Florence A. Dees

GORDON

P.O. Box 337
Calhoun, GA 30703-0337
(706) 629-9242
Peggy L. Smith

GRADY

250 N. Broad St.
Cairo, GA 31728
(912) 377-3322
Janice P. Womble

GREENE

Courthouse
113B N. Main St.
Greensboro, GA 30642
(706) 453-3358
Samuel A. Gutherie

GWINNETT

75 Langley Drive
Lawrencville, GA 30245-6900
(770) 822-7324
Katherine L. Sherrington

HABRESHAM

P.O. Box 166
Clarksville, GA 30523-0166
(404) 754-2516
Rhoda Seabolt

HALL

P.O. Box 1579
Gainesville, GA 30503-1579
(770) 531-6957
Donald A. Elrod

HANCOCK

602 Broad St.
Sparta, GA 31807
(706) 444-5148
Herbert Brunson

HARALSON

P.O. Box 330
Buchanan, GA 30113-0152
(770) 646-2020
Barbara G. Ridley

HARRIS

P.O. Box 152
Hamilton, GA 31811-0
(706) 628-4843
Sarah McDowell

HART

P.O. Drawer 748
Hartwell, GA 30643-0748
(706) 376-3944
Philip Hix

HEARD

P.O. Box 519
Franklin, GA 30217-0519
(706) 675-3391
Sandra Turner-Nolen

HENRY

P.O. Box 675
McDonough, GA 30253-0675
(770)954-2470
Andy Pipkin

HOUSTON

P.O. Drawer 7799
Warner Robins, GA 31095
Juanita Mason

IRWIN

Box 645
Ocilla, GA 31774-0645
(912) 468-5505
Sandra D. Paulk

JACKSON

P.O. Box 247
Jefferson, GA 30549-0247
(706) 367-1199

JASPER

Courthouse
Monticello, GA 31064
(706)468-4941
Merry Faulkner

Jeff Davis
P.O. Box 558
Hazlehurst, GA 31539-0558
(912) 375-6622

JEFFERSON

P.O. Box 426
Louisville, GA 30434-0426
(912)625-7736
Jenny Weeks

JENKINS

P.O. box 646
Millen, GA 30442-0646
(912) 982-4925
Brenda B. Mathern

JOHNSON

P.O.Box 163
Wrightsviole, GA 31096-0163
(912) 864-2565
Sherry Vickers

JONES

County Government Center
Industrial Blvd.
Gray, GA 31032
Brian Jackson

LAMAR

130 Library St.
Barnesville, GA 30204-1699
(770) 358-5162
Geraldine Pippin

LANIER

Courthouse
100 Main St.
Lakeland, GA 31634-1190
(912) 482-3795
Joe P. Carter

LAURENS

P.O. Box 2099
Dublin, GA 31040-2099
(912) 272-6994

LEE

P.O. box 9
Leesburg, GA 31763-0009
(912) 759-6015
Martha C. Johnson

LIBERTY

P.O. Box 587
Hinesville, GA 31313-0587
(912) 876-3389
Carolyn R. Brown

LINCOLN

P.O. Box 185
Lincolnton, GA 30817-0340
(706) 359-4444
Brenda T. Danner

LONG

P.O. Box 628
Ludowici, GA 31316-0628
(912) 545-2127
Lillian G. Simmons

LOWNDES

Box 1409
Valdosta, GA 31603-1409
(912) 333-5108
Paul E. Sumner

LUMPKIN

99 Courthouse Hill
Dahlonega, GA 30533
(706) 864-2666
Jean F. Grizzle

MACON

P.O. Box 485
Oglethorpe, GA 31068-0485
(912) 472-7031
Rhonda S. Respress

MADISON

Box 217
Danielsville, GA 30633=0217
(706) 795-3351
Louise Watson

MARION

P.O. Box 219
Buena Vista, GA 31803-0219
(912) 649-5231
Judith Smith

MCDUFFIE

P.O Box 955
Thomson,GA 30824-0955
(706) 595-2132
Cathy Kitchens

MCINTOSH

P.O. Box 571
Darien, GA 31305-0571
(912) 437-6627
Sheila A. Atkinson

MERIWETHER

P.O. Box 729
Greenville, GA 30222-0729
(706) 672-4219
Herbert Y. Johnson

MILLER

P.O. Box 65
Colquitt, GA 31737-0065
(912) 758-4101
Carolyn Worsley

MITCHELL

P.O. Box 373
Camilla, GA 31730-0373
(912) 336-2010
Alberta C. Fowler

MONROE

Box 357
Forsyth, GA 31029-0357
(912) 994-7020
Patsy J. Miller

MONTGOMERY

P.O. Box317
Mt. Vernon, GA 30445-0317
(912)583-2571
Lawana M. Sharpe

MORGAN

Courthouse, Rm. 110
Madison, GA 30650
(706) 342-0464
Brenda B. White

MURRAY

P.O. Box 336
Chatsworth, GA 30705-0336
(706) 695-3423
Charlotte Hooper-Keener

MUSCOGEE

P.O. Box 1441
Columbus, GA 31902-1441
(706) 571-5852
Lula L. Huff

NEWTON

1105 Usher St.
Covington, GA 30209
(770) 784-2020
Carol B. Harris

OCONEE

P.O. Box 106
Watkinsville, GA 30677-0106
(706) 769-3917
Harriette M. Browning

OGLETHORPE

Box 305
Lexington, GA 30648-0305
(706) 743-8422
Jeannie P. Fincher

PAULDING

25 Courthouse Square
Rm. 203 Annex
Dallas GA 30132-1494
(770) 443-7581

PEACH

P.O. Box 931
Fort Valley, GA 31030-0931
(912)825-3161
Dwight S. Byrd

PICKENS

52 N. Main St., Suite 205
Jasper, GA 30143-1598
(706) 692-2021
Rachel Goss

PIERCE

P.O. Drawer 192
Blackshear, GA 31516-0192
(912) 449-2026
Jesse Lewis

PIKE

P.O. Box 217
Zebulon, GA 30295-0217
(770) 567-2001
Donna M Wynn

POLK

Courthouse Rm. 101
Cedartown, GA 30125
(770) 749-2125
Dan F. Casey , Sr.

PULASKI

P.O. Box 448
Hawkinsville, GA 31036-1350
(912) 783-2811
Diane D. Lnacaster

PUTNAM

108 S. Madison Ave., #100
Eatonton, GA 31024-1089
(706) 485-5441
June McLeroy

QUITMAN

P.O. Box 35
Georgetown, GA 31754-0035
(912) 334-9000
Theresa D. Balkcom

RABUN

P.O. Box 806
Clayton, GA 30525-0806
(706) 782-3613
Icie Green Hamilton

RANDOLPH

P.O. Box 323
Cuthbert, GA 31740-0323
(912)732-2881
Carolyn D. Taylor

RICHMOND

117 City County Building
Augusta, GA 30911-3999
(706) 821-2391
Jerome Saul

ROCKDALE

P.o. Drawer 1497
Conyers, GA 30207-1497
(912)937-2689
Dan Ray

SCHLEY

P.O. Box 327
Ellaville, GA 31806-0327
(912) 937-2689
Pam G. Register

SCREVEN

P.O. Box 86
Sylvania, GA 30467-0086
(912) 564-2206
Donald Jamerson Jr.

SEMINOLE

County Courthouse
Donaldsonville, GA 31745
(912) 524-2238
Gloria H. Fain

SPALDING

P.O. Box 186
Griffin, GA 30224-0186
(770) 467-4360
Sylvia W. Hollums

STEPHENS

P.O. Box 187
Toccoa, GA 30577-0187
(706) 886-4753
Vickie Whitworth

STEWART

P.O. Box 245
Lumpkin, GA 31815-0245
(912) 838-4247
Kay Skellie

SUMTER

P.O. Box 1044
Americus, GA 31709-1044
(912) 924-5749
Dan McGowan

TALBOT

P.O. Box 147
Talbotton, GA 31827-0147
(706) 665-3240
William Huff

TALIAFERRO

P.O. Box 139
Crawfordville, GA 30631-0139
(706) 456-2520
Ian Macfie

TATTNALL

P.O. Box 920
Reidsville, GA 30453-0920
(912) 557-6736
Don P. Cobb

TAYLOR

P.O. Box 446
Butler, GA 31006-0446
(912) 862-3637
Peggy Wilson

TELFAIR

Courthouse Square
McRae, GA 31055-1604
(912) 868-6545
Rosa Willialmson

TERRELL

P.O. Box 484
Dawson, GA 31742-0484
(12) 995-5151
Peggy H. Pritchard

THOMAS

P.O. Box 2175
Thomsville, GA 31799-2175
(912)225-4136
Shirley Prevatt

TIFT

P.O. Box 930
Tifton, GA 31793-0930
(912) 386-7820
Mitchell E. Goode

TOOMBS

P.O Boxe 458
Lyons, GA 30436-04588
(912) 526-8575
Glenda Williams

TOWNS

48 River St., Suite H
Hiawassee, GA 30546
(706) 896-2267
Bruce Wilson

TREUTLEN

P.O. Box 123
Soperton, GA 30457-0123
(912)529-3213
Wayne Sumner

TROUP

P.O. Box 1149
Lagrange, GA 30241-1149
(706) 883-1620
Ellis C. Smith

TURNER

P.O Box 846.
Ashburn, GA 31714-0846
(912) 567-3636
Charles F. Evans

TWIGGS

P.O. Box 187
Jeffersonville, GA 31044-0187
(912)945-3359
E. Walton Nesmith

UNION

114 Courthouse St. , Box 3
Blairsville, GA 30512
(706) 745-2881
J.W. Payne

UPSON

P.O. Box 409
Thomaston, GA 30286-0409
(706) 647-8932
Cherie C. Greene

WALKER

Box 628
Lafayette, GA 30728-0628
(706) 638-2929
Melba T. Powell

WALTON

P.O. Box 767
Monroe, GA 30655
(770) 267-1474
Mearon Queen

WARE

Courthouse, Rm. 109
Waycross, GA 31501-3594
(912)287-4305
Faye W. Booth

WARREN

P.O. Box 189
Warrenton, GA 30828-0189
(706) 465-2231
Lynette Johnson

WASHINGTON

Box 469
Sandersville, GA 31082-0469
(912) 552-2144
Connie Tapley

WAYNE

P.O. Box 287
Jesup, GA 31598-0287
(912) 427-5910
Al Szoke

WEBSTER

P.O. Box 73
Preston, GA 31824
(912) 828-3690
Lou Heath

WHEELER

P.O. Box 431
Alamo, GA 30411-0431
(912)568-7131
Janice A. Nobles

WHITE

59 S. Main St., Suite C
Cleveland, GA 30528
(706) 865-2225
J.H. Tow, Jr.

WHITFIELD

300 W. Crawford St..
Dalton, GA 30720-4296
(706) 275-7510
Danny Sane

WILCOX

Courthouse
103 N. Broad St.
Abbeville, GA 31001-1000
(912) 467-2025
Bobby H. Gibbs

WILKES

25 E. Court St., Rm. 204
Washington, GA 30673-1593
(706) 678-2422
Mary W. Hubbard

WILKINSON

P.O. Box 182
Irwinton, GA 31042-0182
(912) 946-2232
Kevin L. Rauscher

WORTH

201 North Main St., Rm. 15
Sylvester, GA 31791
(912) 776-8204
Tony McDonald

THIS PAGE INTENTIONALLY LEFT BLANK FOR NOTES

Hawaii

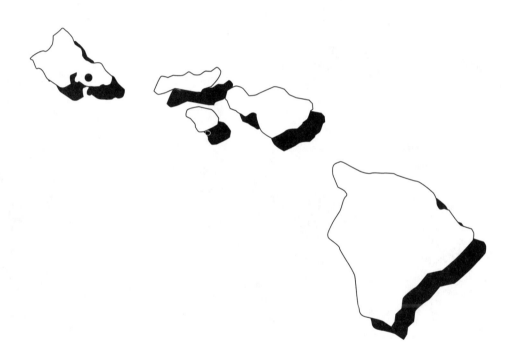

HAWAII

HAWAII LAND COURT

City & County of Honolulu
Real Property Collection Unit
Division of Treasury
P.O. Box 4200
Honolulu, HI 96812
(808) 587-0121

FIRST CIRCUIT COURTHOUSE

Kaahumanu Hale
842 Bethel St., 2nd Floor
Honolulu, HI 96813
(808) 527-5502

SECOND CIRCUIT COURTHOUSE

1580 Kaahumanu Ave.
Wailuku, HI 96793
(808) 243-7697
(808) 243-7884

THIRD CIRCUIT COURTHOUSE

State Building
865 Piilent St.
Hilo, HI 96720
(808) 961-8282

FIFTH CIRCUIT COURTHOUSE

Real Propety Tax Collector
4444 Rice St., Suite 463
Lihue, HI 96766
(808) 241-6555

Idaho

IDAHO

Number of Counties: 44

ADA

Phone: (208) 364-2233
Barbara Bauer (R)
Box 2868,
Boise, ID 83701

BANNOCK

Phone: (208) 236-7220
Delinquent Property Tax Division
P.O. Box 4626
Pocatello, ID 83205-4626
Shelly Shannon

BINGHAM

Phone: (208) 785-5005 ext. 259
P.O. Box 190
Blackfoot, ID 83221
Audrey Porter

BONNER

Phone: (208) 265-1433
215 S. First Ave.
Sandpoint ID 83864
Shannon Syth (R)

BONNEVILLE

Phone: (208) 529-1360 ext. 1380
c/o Treasurer's Office
605 N. Capital Ave.
Idaho Falls, 83402
Lila Jordan (R)

ADAMS

Phone: (208) 253-4263
Delinquent Property Tax Division
P.O. Box 47
Council, ID 83612-0048
Nancy Armitage

BEAR LAKE

Phone: (208) 945-2130
Delinquent Property Tax Division
P.O. Box 55
Paris, ID 83261-0055
Nola F. Jones

BENAWAH

Phone: (208) 245-2421
Delinquent Property Tax Division
701 College Ave.
St. Maries ID 83861
Juanita Lundt

BLAINE

Phone: (208) 788-5530
P.O. Box 905
Hailey, ID 83333
Vicki Dick

BOISE

Phone: (208) 392-4441
P.O. Box BC
Idaho City, ID 83631
Carlyne Reed

BOUNDARY

Phone: (208) 267-3291
P.O. Box 218
Bonners Ferry, ID 83805
Wilma DeVore

CUSTER

Phone: (208) 879-2330
Delinquent Property Tax Division
P.O. Box 350
Challis, ID 83226-0385
Judy Leuzinger

ELMORE

Phone: (208) 587-2138
Delinquent Property Tax Division
150 S. 4th East Suite 4
Mt. Home, ID 83647
Carol Olds

FRANKLIN

Phone: (208) 852-1095
Delinquent Property Tax Division
39 W. Oneida
Preston, ID 83263
Maureen Ainscough

FREMONT

Phone: (208) 624-3361
Delinquent Property Tax Division
151 W. 1st North, Rm. 11
St. Anthony, ID 83445
Pat McCoy

GEM

Phone: (208) 365-3272
Delinquent Property Tax Division
415 E. Main St.
Emmett, ID 83617
Marilyn Fraiser

LEWIS

Phone: (208) 937-2341
Delinquent Property Tax Division
P.O. Box 100
Nezperce, ID 83543
Mary Lou Puckett

LINCOLN

Phone: (208) 886-7681
Delinquent Property Tax Division
P.O. Box 725
Shoshone, ID 83352
Kathy Quiroga

MADISON

Phone: (208) 356-6871
Delinquent Property Tax Division
P.O. Box 65
Rexburg, ID 83440
Sherry Arnold

MINIDOKA

Phone: (208) 436-7188
Delinquent Property Tax Division
P.O. Box 474
Rupert, ID 83350
Laura Twiss

ONEIDA

Phone: (208) 766-2962
Delinquent Property Tax Division
10 Court St.
Malad City, ID 83252
Dianne Pett

OWYHEE

Phone: 495-1158
Box 128
Murphy, ID 83650
Barbara Wright

CANYON

Phone: (208) 454-7354
P.O. Box 1010
Caldwell, ID 83606
Tracie Lloyd

KOOTENAI

Phone: (208) 769-4455
Delinquent Property Tax Division
P.O. Box 9000
Coeur d'lene ID 83816501 Government Way
Jeannine Ashcraft

LATAH

Phone: (208) 883-2252
P.O. Box 8068
Moscow, ID 83843-0568
NonaRae Robinson

NEZ PERCE

Phone: (208) 799-3030
Delinquent Property Tax Division
P.O. Box 896
Lewiston, ID 83501-0896
Rena Crisp

TWIN FALLS

Phone: (208) 736-4000 ext.
Delinquent Property Tax Division
P.O. Box 88
Twin Falls, ID 83303-0088
Bonnie Bruning

BUTTE

Phone: (208) 527-3047
Delinquent Property Tax Division
P.O. Box 121
Arco, ID 83213-0727
Lorie Beck

CAMAS

Phone: (208) 764-2126
Delinquent Property Tax Division
P.O. Box 430
Fairfield, ID 83327-0430
Sally Pridmore

CARIBOU

Phone: (208) 547-3726
Delinquent Property Tax Division
P.O. Box 507
Soda Springs, ID 83276
Diane Meads

CASSIA

Phone: (208) 678-7202
Cassia County Courthouse
Delinquent Property Tax Division
Burley, ID 83318
Gayle Erikson

CLARK

Phone: (208) 374-5455
Delinquent Property Tax Division
P.O. Box 266
Dubois, ID 83423-0205
Bonnie Burns

CLEARWATER

Phone: (208) 476-5213
Delinquent Property Tax Division
P.O. Box 707
Orofino, ID 83544
Jeannie Johnson

GOODING

Phone: (208) 934-5673
Delinquent Property Tax Division
624 Main St.
Gooding, ID 83330
Helen Faulkner

IDAHO

Phone: (208) 983-2801
Idaho County Courthouse
Delinquent Property Tax Division
320 W. Main, Rm 2
Grangeville, ID 83530
Sharon Cox

JEFFERSON

Phone: (208) 745-9219
Delinquent Property Tax Division
134 N. Clark
Rigby, ID 83442-0275
Margaret Treasure

JEROME

Phone: (208) 324-7594
Delinquent Property Tax Division
300 N. Lincoln, Suite 209
Jerome, ID 83338
Mary Childers

LEMHI

Phone: (208) 756-2816
Delinquent Property Tax Division
206 Courthouse Dr.
Salmon, ID 83467
Maryanne Heiser

PAYETTE

Phone: (208) 642-6004
1130 3rd Ave. N.
Payette, ID 83661
Wanda Collingwood

POWER

Phone: (208) 226-7614
Delinquent Property Tax Division
543 Bannock Ave.
American Falls, ID 83211
Julie Zacharias

SHOSHONE

Phone: (208) 752-1261
Delinquent Property Tax Division
700 Bank St.
Wallace, ID 83873
Tammy House

TETON

Phone: (208) 354-2254
Delinquent Property Tax Division
P.O. Box 177
Driggs, ID 83422
Bonnie Hatch

VALLEY

Phone: (208) 382-4293
Delinquent Property Tax Division
P.O. Box 738
Cascade, ID 83611
Diana Healy

WASHINGTON

Phone: (208) 549-0324
Delinquent Property Tax Division
256 E. Court St.
Weiser, ID 83672
Pat Harberd

THIS PAGE INTENTIONALLY LEFT BLANK FOR NOTES

Kansas

KANSAS

Number of Counties: 105

BARTON

Phone: (316) 793-1827
FAX: (316) 793-1807
400 Main St.
P.O. Box 1130
Great Bend, KS 67530
Jenneth Hallmark

BUTLER

Phone: (316) 322-4215
FAX: (316) 321-1011
205 West Central
El Dorado, KS 6704
Beverly Lefever

COWLEY

Phone: (316) 221-5412
FAX: (316) 221-5448
Delinquent Property Tax Division
311 E. 9th St
P.O. Box 744
Winfield, KS 67156
Patty McDonald

CRAWFORD

Phone: (316) 724-8222
Fax: (316) 724-8823
P.O. Box 96
Girard, KS 66743
John Kovacic

DOUGLAS

Phone: (913) 841-7700
Fax: (913) 832-0226
Delinquent Property Tax Division
P.O. Box 884
Lawrence, KS 66044-0884
Nancy Hempen

ELLIS

Phone: (913) 628-9465
Fax: (913) 628-9467
P.O. Box 520
Hays, KS 67601
Mike Billinger

FINNEY

Phone: (316) 272-3526
Fax: (316) 272-3599
Finney County Courthouse
425 N. 8th
Garden City, KS 67846
Raylene Nelson

FORD

Phone: (316) 227-4536
Fax: (316)227-4532
Delinquent Property Tax Division
100 Gunsmoke
Dodge City, KS 67801
Dorothy Hunter

GEARY

Phone: (913) 238-6021
Fax: (913) 238-5419
Delinquent Property Tax Division
139 E. 8th
P.O. Box 825
Junction City, KS 66441
Kathy Tremont

HARVEY

Phone: (316) 284-6980
Fax: (316) 283-4892
Delinquent Property Tax Division
8th & Main
Newton, KS 67114
Jim Reber

JOHNSON

Phone: (913) 764-8484 ext.5355
Fax: (913) 791-5360
111 S. Cherry St., Suite 1500
Olathe, KS 66061-3441
William O'Brien

LABETTE

Phone: (316) 795-2918 ext. 230
Fax: (316) 795-2928
Delinquent Property Tax Division
516 Merchant
P.O. Box 388
Oswego, KS 67356
Barbara Goodnight

LEAVENWORTH

Phone: (913) 684-0432
Fax: (913) 684-0406
Delinquent Property Tax Division
Leavenworth County Treasurer
300 Walnut
Leavenworth, KS 66048
Shirley Tate

LYON

Phone: (316) 342-4950
Fax: (316) 342-2662
Delinquent Property Tax Division
P.O. Box 747
4th & Com'l
Emporia, KS 66801
Dora Hartig

MCPHERSON

Phone: (316) 241-3664
Fax: (316) 241-7040
Delinquent Property Tax Division
P.O. Box 1206
McPherson, KS 67460
Brenda Becker

MONTGOMERY

Phone: (316) 331-3040
Fax: (316) 331-1686
Box 767
Independence, KS 67301
Billie Lewark

RENO

Phone: (316) 694-2938
Fax: (316) 694-2944
206 West 1st
Hutchinson, KS 67504-2067
Larry Tucker

RILEY

Phone: (913) 537-6324
Fax: (913) 537-6326
Delinquent Property Tax Division
110 Courthouse Plaza
Manhattan, KS 66502
Eileen King

SALINE

Phone: (913) 826-6545
Fax: (913) 826-6629
300 W. Ash
Salina, KS 67401-5040
Keith Lilly

SEDGWICK

Phone: (316) 383-7707
Fax: (316) 383-7713
Delinquent Property Tax Division
P.O. Box 3412
Wichita, KS 67201
Jerry McCoy

SHAWNEE

Phone: (913) 233-8200
Fax: (913) 233-291-4900
Delinquent Property Tax Division
200 E. 7th St., Rm. 103
Topeka, KS 66603
Rita Cline

SUMNER

Phone: (316) 326-3371
Fax: (316)326-8172
Delinquent Property Tax Division
500 N. Washington P.O. Box 190
Wellington, KS 67152
Betty Showers

WYANDOTTE

Phone: (913) 573-2823
Fax:(913) 321-0237
Delinquent Property Tax Division
710 N. 7th St.
Kansas City, KS 66101
Mary Labesic

ALLEN

Phone: (316) 365-1409
Fax: (316) 365-1414
Delinquent Property Tax Division
1 N. Washington
Iola, KS 66749
Betty Daniels

ANDERSON

Phone: (913) 448-5824
Fax: (913) 448-5621
Delinquent Property Tax Division
100 E. 4th Courthouse
Garnett, KS 66032
Dena McDaniel

ATCHISON

Phone: (913) 367-5332
Fax: (913) 367-5332
423 N. 5th
Atchison, KS 66002
Dolores Ebling

BARBER

Phone: (316) 886-3775
Fax: (316) 886-5425
Delinquent Property Tax Division
120 E. Washington
Medicine Lodge, KS 67104
Linda Hamilton

BOURBON

Phone: (316) 223-3800
Fax: (316)223-5421
Delinquent Property Tax Division
210 S. National
Fort Scott, KS 66701
Opal Hess

BROWN

Phone: (913) 742-2051
Fax: (913) 742-3255
Delinquent Property Tax Division
601 Oregon
Hiawatha, KS 66434
Deborah Rowland

CHASE

Phone: (316) 273-6493
Fax: (316) 273-6617
Delinquent Property Tax Division
P.O. Box 206 (Pearl & Broadway)
Cottonwood Falls, KS 66845
Karen Crighton

CHAUTAUQUA

Phone: (316) 725-3666
Fax (316) 725-3256
Delinquent Property Tax Division
215 N. Chautauque
Sedan, KS 67361
Karen Thompson

CHEROKEE

Phone: (316) 429-3848
Fax: (316) 429-2256
P.O. Box 149
County Courthouse
Columbus, KS 66725
Hazel Kresyman

CHEYENNE

Phone: (913) 332-2252
Fax: (913) 332-2274
Delinquent Property Tax Division
P.O. Box 687
St. Francis, KS 67756
Gladys Cook

CLARK

Phone: (316) 635-2745
Fax: (316) 635-2393
Delinquent Property Tax Division
913 Highland
Ashland, KS 67831
Colleen Brown

CLAY

Phone: (913) 632-3282
Fax: (913) 632-3619
Delinquent Property Tax Division
P.O. Box 75
Clay Center, KS 67432
Vicki Jenkins

CLOUD

Phone: (913) 243-8115
Fax: (913)243-8123
Delinquent Property Tax Division
P.O. Box 355
811 Washington
Concordia, KS 66901
Alice Walker

COFFEY

Phone: (316) 364-5532
Fax: (316) 364-8643
Delinquent Property Tax Division
110 S. 6th St., Rm. 203
Burlington, KS 66839
Joann Raaf

COMANCHE

Phone: (316) 582-2964
Fax: (316)5822426
Delinquent Property Tax Division
P.O. Box 246
201 S. New York
Coldwater, KS 67029
Patty Fose

DECATUR

Phone: (913) 475-8103
Fax: (913) 475-8150
Delinquent Property Tax Division
94 S. Penn
Oberlin, KS 67749
Pat Fringer

DICKINSON

Phone: (913) 263-3231
Fax: (913) 263-1512
Delinquent Property Tax Division
1st & Buckeye Sts.
Abilene, KS 67410
Louise Habacker

DONIPHAN

Phone: (913) 985-3831
Fax: (913) 985-3723
P.O. Box 308
Troy, KS 66087
Jackie Linck

EDWARDS

Phone: (316) 659-3132
Fax: (316) 659-2583
Delinquent Property Tax Division
P.O. Box 246
300 Mass.
Kinsley, KS 67547
Mary Carlson

ELK

Phone: (316) 374-2256
Fax: (316) 374-2246
Delinquent Property Tax Division
P.O. Box 325
Howard, KS 67349
Pat Robertson

ELLSWORTH

Phone: (913) 472-4152
Fax: (913) 472-4912
Delinquent Property Tax Division
210 N. Kansas
Ellsworth, KS 67439
Paula Schneider

FRANKLIN

Phone: (913) 242-4201
Fax: (913) 242-8162
Delinquent Property Tax Division
315 S. Main St.
Ottawa, KS 66067
Juanita Zeek

GOVE

Phone: (913) 674-2331
Fax: (913) 938-4486
Delinquent Property Tax Division
Gove Co. Government Bldg.
Gove, KS 67736
Cheryl Remington

GRAHAM

Phone: (913) 674-2331
Fax: (913) 674-5463
Delinquent Property Tax Division
410 N. Pomeroy
Hill City, KS 67642
Jerilyn Keith

GRANT

Phone: (316) 356-1551
Fax: (316) 356-3886
Delinquent Property Tax Division
108 S. Glenn
Ulysses, KS 67880
Rita Gee

GRAY

Phone: (316) 855-3861
Fax: (316) 885-3107
Delinquent Property Tax Division
300 S. Main
Cimmarron, KS 67835-0487
Sheryl Evinger

GREELEY

Phone: (316) 376-4413
Fax: (316) 376-2574
Delinquent Property Tax Division
P.O. Box 207
Tribuen, KS 67879
Diane Gentry

GREENWOOD

Phone; (316) 583-7446
Fax: (316)583-7297
311 N. Main St.
Eureka, KS 67045
Sue Williams

HAMILTON

Phone: (316) 384-5522
Fax: (316)384-5853
Delinquent Property Tax Division
219 N. Main
Syracuse, KS 67878
Chris Squire

HARPER

Phone: (316) 842-5191
Fax: (316) 842-3455
Delinquent Property Tax Division
Harper County Courthouse
Anthony, KS 67003
Carmen Alldritt

HASKELL

Phone: (316) 675-8548
Fax: (316) 675-8142
Delinquent Property Tax Division
P.O. Box 578
Sublette, KS 67877
Nancy Weeks

HODGEMAN

Phone: (316) 357-6236
Fax: (316) 357-8300
Delinquent Property Tax Division
P.O. Box 247
Jetmore, KS 67854
Melody Vieux

JACKSON

Phone: (913) 364-5262
Fax: (913) 364-3420
400 New York Ave. Room 206
Delinquent Property Tax Division
Holton, KS 66436
Marilyn Brown

JEFFERSON

Phone: (913) 863-2691
Fax: (913) 863-3041
Delinquent Property Tax Division
P.O. Box 458
Oskaloosa, KS 66066
Caralyn Casebier

JEWELL

Phone: (913) 378-3700
Fax: (913) 378-4075
07 N. Commercial
Delinquent Property Tax Division
Mankato, KS 66956

KEARNEY

Phone: (316) 355-6372
Fax: (316) 355-7382
Delinquent Property Tax Division
04 N. Main Box 146
P.O. Box 146
Lakin, KS 67860
Holly Lashmet

KINGMAN

Phone: (316) 532-3461
Fax: (316) 532-3732
Delinquent Property Tax Division
130 N. Spruce
Kingman, KS 67068
Deanna Krehbiel

KIOWA

Phone: (316) 723-2681
Fax: (316) 723-3302
Delinquent Property Tax Division
211 E. Florida
Greensburg, KS 67054
Elsie Haraldson

LANE

Phone: (316) 397-2802
Fax: (316) 397-5937
Delinquent Property Tax Division
44 S. Lane
Dighton, KS 67839
Patricia Sharp

LINCOLN

Phone: (913) 524-4757
Fax: (913) 524-4108
216 E. Lincoln Ave.
Lincoln, KS 67455
Joyce Walker

LINN

Phone: (913) 795-2227
Fax: (913) 795-2889
Linn County Courthouse
Delinquent Property Tax Division
315 Main
Mound City, KS 66056
Patricia Davie

LOGAN

Phone: (913) 672-3216
Fax: (913) 672-3517
Delinquent Property Tax Division
710 W. 2nd
Oakley, KS 67748
Kay Marcy

MARION

Phone: (316) 382-2180
Fax: (316) 382-3420
Delinquent Property Tax Division
200 S. 3rd Street P.O. Box 257
Marion, KS 66861
Jenine Bateman

MARSHALL

Phone: (913) 562-5363
Fax: (913) 562-5421
Delinquent Property Tax Division
1201 Broadway, Rm. 1
Marysville, KS 66508
Caralyn Arginbright

MEADE

Phone: (316) 873-8740
Fax: (316) 873-8713
Delinquent Property Tax Division
P.O. Box 660
Meade, KS 67864
Wynema Dye

MIAMI

Phone: (913) 294-2353
Fax: (913) 294-9515
Delinquent Property Tax Division
P.O. Box 228
20 S. Pearl
Paola, KS 66071
Mary Lou Bricker

MITCHELL

Phone: (913) 738-3411
Fax: (913) 738-5844
Delinquent Property Tax Division
P.O. Box 425
13 S. Hersey
Beloit, KS 67420
Carol Emmot

MORRIS

Phone: (316) 767-5617
Fax: (316) 767-6861
Delinquent Property Tax Division
501 W. Main
Council Grove, KS 66846
Shirley Thurston

MORTON

Phone: (316) 697-2560
Fax: (316) 697-2159
Delinquent Property Tax Division
1025 Morton Street
Elkhart, KS 67950
Lois Hall

NEMAHA

Phone: (913) 336-2106
Fax: (913) 336-3373
Delinquent Property Tax Division
607 Nemaha
Seneca, KS 66538
Rosemary Wilhelm

NEOSHO

Phone: (316) 244-3800
Fax: (316) 244-3860
Delinquent Property Tax Division
100 South Maine
Erie, KS 66733
Charla Sands

NESS

Phone: (913) 798-3300
Fax: (913) 798-3829
Delinquent Property Tax Division
P.O. Box 56
Ness City, KS 67560
David Jarvis

NORTON

Phone: (913) 877-5795
Fax: (913) 877-5722
Delinquent Property Tax Division
P.O. Box 70
105 S. Kansas
Norton, KS 67654
Cynthia Linner

OSAGE

Phone: (913) 828-4923
Fax: (913) 828-3336
Delinquent Property Tax Division
P.O. Box 210
717 Topeka Ave.
Lyndon, KS 66451
Joann Hamilton

OSBORNE

Phone: (913) 346-2251
Fax: (913) 346-5992
Delinquent Property Tax Division
423 W. Main
Osborne, KS 67473
Dara Linton

OTTAWA

Phone: (913) 392-3605
Fax: (913) 392-3659
Delinquent Property Tax Division
307 N. Concord; Suite 270
Minneapolis, KS 67467
Pat Baccus

PAWNEE

Phone: (316) 285-3746
Fax:(316) 285-3746
Delinquent Property Tax Division
715 Broadway
Larned, KS 67550
Kathy Jadwin

PHILLIPS

Phone: (913) 543-6895
Fax: (913) 5436897
Delinquent Property Tax Division
P.O. Box 372
Phillipsburg, KS 67661

POTTAWATOMIE

Phone: (913) 457-2832
Fax: (913) 457-3507
106 Main
Westmoreland, KS 66549
Linda Horgan

PRATT

Phone: (316) 672-4118
Fax: (316) 672-9541
Delinquent Property Tax Division
P.O. Box 905
Pratt, KS 67124
Donna Shelite

RAWLINS

Phone: (913) 626-3331
Fax: (913)626-9019
Delinquent Property Tax Division
P.O. Box 182
607 Main
Atwood, KS 67730
Cheryl Wederski

REPUBLIC

Phone: (913) 527-5691 ext. 234
Fax: (913) 527-2717
Delinquent Property Tax Division
P.O. Box 429
1811 M St.
Belleville, KS 66935
Emma Berggren

RICE

Phone: (316) 257-2852
Fax: (316) 257-2852
Delinquent Property Tax Division
01 W. Commerical
Lyons, KS 67564
Lila Blackburn

ROOKS

Phone: (913) 425-6161
Fax: (913) 425-7124
Delinquent Property Tax Division
114 N. Walnut
Stockton, KS 67669
Eleanor Buss

RUSH

Phone: (913) 222-3416
Fax: (913) 222-3559
Delinquent Property Tax Division
P.O. Box 460
LaCrosse, KS 67548
Christy Bittel

RUSSELL

Phone: (913) 483-2251
Fax: (913) 483-5725
Delinquent Property Tax Division
Russell County Courthouse
401 Main P.O. Box 855
Russell, KS 67665
Judy Corley

SCOTT

Phone: (316) 872-2640
Fax: (316) 872-7145
Delinquent Property Tax Division
303 Court St.
Scott City, KS 67871
Lark Spear

SEWARD

Phone: (316) 626-3213
Fax: (316) 626-3306
Seward County Courthouse
415 N. Washington, Suite 113
Liberal, KS 67901
Amy Jo Neese

SHERIDAN

Phone: (913) 675-3622
Fax: (913) 675-3050
Delinquent Property Tax Division
925 9th Street
Hoxie, KS 67740
Esther Bainter

SHERMAN

Phone: (913) 899-4810
Fax: (913) 899-4848
Delinquent Property Tax Division
813 Broadway, Rm. 103
Goodland, KS 67735
Shelby Miller

SMITH

Phone: (913) 282-5170
Fax: (913) 282-5175
Delinquent Property Tax Division
218 S. Grant
Smith Center, KS 66967
Harry Jones, III

STAFFORD

Phone: (316) 549-3508
Fax: (316) 549-6409
Delinquent Property Tax Division
209 N. Broadway
St. John, KS 67576
Lynda McAlister

STANTON

Phone: (316) 492-2160
Fax: (316) 492-2688
Delinquent Property Tax Division
P.O. Box 520
200 N. Main
Johnson, KS 67855
Phyllis Kistler

STEVENS

Phone: (316) 544-2542
Fax: (316) 544-4081
Delinquent Property Tax Division
200 E. 6th St.
Hugoton, KS 67951
Belva Hickey

THOMAS

Phone: (913) 462-4520
Fax: (913) 462-4512
P.O. Box 828t
Colby, KS 67701
Donita Applebury

TREGO

Phone: (913) 743-2001
Fax: (913) 743-2461
Delinquent Property Tax Division
P.O. Box 356
Wakeeney, KS 67672
Gary Watson

WABAUNSEE

Phone: (913) 765-3812
Fax: (913) 765-3992
Delinquent Property Tax Division
215 Kansas
Alma, KS 66401
Ella May Kraus

WALLACE

Phone: (913) 852-4281
Fax: (913) 852-4783
Delinquent Property Tax Division
313 Main   P.O. Box 40
Sharon Springs, KS 67758
Viola Rohn

WASHINGTON

Phone: (913) 325-2830
Fax: (913) 325-2461
Delinquent Property Tax Division
214 C St.
Washington, KS 66968
Alice Faye Baird

WICHITA

Phone: (316) 375-2715
Fax: (316) 375-4350
Delinquent Property Tax Division
P.O. Box 488
206 4th St.
Leoti, KS 67861
Sharen Altman

WILSON

Phone: (316) 378-2775
Fax: (316) 378-4510
Delinquent Property Tax Division
615 Madison St.
Fredonia, KS 66736
Rita Githens

WOODSON

Phone: (316) 625-3252
Fax: (316) 625-2557
Delinquent Property Tax Division
105 W. Rutledge
Yates Center, KS 66783
Ray Hite

WYANDOTTE

Phone: (913) 573-2823
Fax: (919) 321-0237
Delinquent Property Tax Division
10 N. 7th
ansas City, KS 66101
Yates Center, KS 66783
Ray Hite

Louisiana

LOUISIANA

Number of Counties: 64

ACADIA

Phone: (318) 788-8750
Delinquent Property Tax Division
500 E. Court Circle, Rm. 215
P.O. Box 600
Crowley, LA 70527-6001
Sabrina Stutes

ASCENSION

Phone: (504) 473-8630
Delinquent Property Tax Division
P.O. Box 389
Donaldsonville, LA 70346
Mark West

AVOYELLES

Phone: (318) 253-4000
Delinquent Property Tax Division
675 Government
Marksville, LA 71351
Bill Belt

BEAUREGARD

Phone: (318) 462-2400
Delinquent Property Tax Division
P.O. Box 370
de Ridder, LA 70634
M. Boliver Bishop

BOSSIER

Phone: (318) 965-3400
Delinquent Property Tax Division
P.O. Box 8
Benton, LA 71006
Larry C. Deen

CADDO

Phone: (318) 226-6900
501 Texas St., Room 103
Shreveport, LA 71101-5410
Beverly B. Lafitte

CALCASIEU

Phone: (318) 436-5063
Delinquent Property Tax Division
P.O. Box 3287
Lake Charles, LA 70602

DE SOTO

Phone: (318) 872-3610
Delinquent Property Tax Division
P.O. Box 511
Mansfield, LA 71052
Jimmy Stevens

EAST BATON ROUGE

Phone: (504) 389-3920
Delinquent Property Tax Division
222 St. Louis St., Rm. 126
P.O. Box 1471
Baton Rouge, LA 70801
Frank Granger, III

EVANGELINE

Phone: (318) 363-2161
Delinquent Property Tax Division
Evangeline County Courthouse
200 Court St.
Ville Platte, LA 70586
Wayne Morein

IBERIA

Phone: (318) 369-4415
Delinquent Property Tax Division
300 Iberia St.
New Iberia, LA 70560-4587

IBERVILLE

Phone: (504) 687-5132
Delinquent Property Tax Division
58050 Meriam St.
P.O. Box 231
Plaquemine, LA 70764
Marla Medlen

JEFFERSON

Phone: (504) 363-5710
Delinquent Property Tax Division
P.O. Box 130
Gretna, LA 70054
Harry Lee

JEFFERSON DAVIS

Phone: (318) 821-2100
Delinquent Property Tax Division
P.O. Box 863
Jennings, LA 70546
Richard Edwards, Jr.

LAFAYETTE

Phone: (318) 236-5881
Delinquent Property Tax Division
P.O. Drawer 92590
Lafayette, LA 70502
Don Breaux

LAFOURCHE

Phone: (504) 449-4431
Delinquent Property Tax Division
P.O. Drawer 5608
Thibodaux, LA 70302
Craig Weber

LINCOLN

Phone: (318) 251-5120
Delinquent Property Tax Division
P.O. Box 2070
Ruston, LA 71273
Wayne Houch

LIVINGSTON

Phone: (504) 686-2241
Delinquent Property Tax Division
P.O. Box 850
Livingston, LA 70754
Odom Graves

MOREHOUSE

Phone: (318) 281-1914
Delinquent Property Tax Division
Courthouse Plaza
P.O. Box 509
Bastrop, LA 71220
Frank Carrol

NATCHITOCHES

Phone: (318) 352-4104
P.O. Box 266
Natchitoches, LA 71458-0266
Boyd Durr

ORLEANS

Phone: (504) 586-4311
Delinquent Property Tax Division
1300 Perdido St., Rm. 1W21
New Orleans, LA 70112
Walter O'Brien

OUACHITA

Phone: (318) 329-1280
P.O. Box 1803
Monroe, LA 71201-1803
Laymon Godwin

PLAQUEMINES

Phone: (504) 333-4401
Delinquent Property Tax Division
P.O. Box 99
Pointe-a-la-Hache, LA 70082
I.F. Hingle, Jr.

RAPIDES

Phone: (318) 473-6741
Delinquent Property Tax Division
P.O. Box 1150
Alexandria, LA 71309-1150

SABINE

Phone: (318) 256-3482
Delinquent Property Tax Division
P.O. Box 1440
Many, LA 71449
James Brumley, Jr.

ST. BERNARD

Phone: (504) 271-2504
Delinquent Property Tax Division
P.O. Box 168
Chalmette, LA 70044
Jack Stephens

ST. CHARLES

Phone: (504) 783-6237
Delinquent Property Tax Division
P.O. Box 440
Hahnville, LA 70057
Meriel Loupe

ST. JOHN THE BAPTIST

Phone: (504) 652-9513
Delinquent Property Tax Division
1801 W. Airline Highway
P.O. Box 1600
Laplace, LA 70069

ST. LANDRY

Phone: (318) 942-3166
Delinquent Property Tax Division
P.O. Drawer C
Opelousas, LA 70571
Ron Duplechain

ST. MARTIN

Phone: (318) 394-3071
Delinquent Property Tax Division
P.O. Box 247
St. Martinville, LA 70582

ST. MARY

Phone: (318) 828-4100
Delinquent Property Tax Division
P.O. Box 264
Franklin, LA 70538
Sherel Martin, Jr.

ST. TAMMANY

Phone: (504) 892-8181
Delinquent Property Tax Division
P.O. Box 608
Covington, LA 70434
Patrick Canulette

TANGIPAHOA

Phone: (504) 748-8147
P.O. Box 727
Amite, LA 70422
J. Edward Layrisson

TERREBONNE

Phone: (504) 876-2500
Delinquent Property Tax Division
P.O. Box 1670
Houma, LA 70361
Jerry Larpenter

VERMILLION

Phone: (318) 893-0871
Delinquent Property Tax Division
P.O. Box 307
Abbeville, LA 70511-0307
Raywood Lemaire

VERNON

Phone: (318) 238-2167
Delinquent Property Tax Division
P.O. Box 1548
Leesville, LA 71446

WASHINGTON

Phone: (504) 839-7817
Washington County Courthouse
Delinquent Property Tax Division
908 Washington St.
Franklinton, LA 70438
Randy Seal

WEBSTER

Phone: (318) 377-1515
Delinquent Property Tax Division
P.O. Box 877
Minden, LA 71058-0389
Royce McMahon

ALLEN

Phone: (318) 639-4353
Delinquent Property Tax Division
P.O. Box 278
Oberlin, LA 70655
Harold A. Turner

ASSUMPTION

Phone: (504) 369-7281
Delinquent Property Tax Division
P.O. Box 518
Napoleonville, LA 70390

BIENVILLE

Phone: (318) 263-2215
Delinquent Property Tax Division
P.O. Box 479
Arcadia, LA 71001

CALDWELL

Phone: (318) 649-2345
Delinquent Property Tax Division
P.O. Box 60
Columbia, LA 71418
Steven E. May

CAMERON

Phone: (318) 775-5826
Delinquent Property Tax Division
P.O. Drawer A
Cameron, LA 70631
James Savoir

CATAHOULA

Phone: (318) 744-5411
Delinquent Property Tax Division
P.O. Box 603
Harrisonburg, LA 71340
Joe T. Trunzler

CLAIBORNE

Phone: (318) 927-2011
Delinquent Property Tax Division
613 E. Main St.
Homer, LA 71040
Kenneth Volentine

CONCORDIA

Phone: (318) 336-5231
4001 Carter St., Rm. 6
Delinquent Property Tax Division
Vidalia, LA 71373
Randy Maxwell

EAST CARROLL

Phone: (318) 559-2800
Delinquent Property Tax Division
400 1st St.
Lake Providence, LA 71254
Dale Rinicker

EAST FELICIANA

Phone: (504) 683-8572
Delinquent Property Tax Division
P.O. Box 207
Clinton, LA 70722
T.R. Maglone

FRANKLIN

Phone: (318) 435-4505
Delinquent Property Tax Division
6556 Main St.
Winnsboro, LA 71295
Eugene Parker

GRANT

Phone: (318) 627-3261
P.O. Box 187
Delinquent Property Tax Division
Colfax, LA 71417
L.R. Hataway

JACKSON

Phone: (318) 259-9021
Jackson County Courthouse
500 E. Court St.
Delinquent Property Tax Division
Jonesboro, LA 71251

LASALLE

Phone: (318) 992-2151
Delinquent Property Tax Division
P.O. Box 70
Jena, LA 71342
Dennis Warwick

MADISON

Phone: (318) 574-1831
Delinquent Property Tax Division
100 N. Cedar St.
Tallulah, LA 71282
C.R. Harman, Jr.

POINTE COUPEE

Phone: (504) 638-5400
Delinquent Property Tax Division
P.O. Box 248
New Roads, LA 70760
Preston Schustz

RED RIVER

Phone: (318) 932-4221
Delinquent Property Tax Division
P.O. Box 375
Coushatta, LA 71019
Buddy Huckabay

RICHLAND

Phone: (318) 728-2071
Delinquent Property Tax Division
708 Julia St.
P.O. Box 668
Rayville, LA 71269
Lorell Graham

ST. HELENA

Phone: (504) 222-4413
Delinquent Property Tax Division
P.O. Box 456
Greensburg, LA 70441
Eugene Holland

ST. JAMES

Phone: (504) 562-7496
Delinquent Property Tax Division
P.O. Box 83
Convent, LA 70723
Willy Martin, Jr.

TENSAS

Phone: (318) 766-3961
Delinquent Property Tax Division
P.O. Box 138
Newelton, LA 71366
Jeff Britt

UNION

Phone: (318) 368-2511
Courthouse Building
Farmerville, LA 71241
Bob Buckley

WEST BATON ROUGE

Phone: (504) 343-9234
Delinquent Property Tax Division
P.O. Box 129
Port Allen, LA 70767
Randall Andre

WEST CARROLL

Phone: (318) 428-2331
Delinquent Property Tax Division
P.O. Drawer 744
Oak Grove, LA 71263
Gary K. Bennett

WEST FELICIANA

Phone: (504) 635-3241
P.O. Drawer 1844
St. Francisville, LA 70775
W.M. Daniel

WINN

Phone: (318) 628-4611
Delinquent Property Tax Division
P.O. Box 950
Winnfield, LA 71483
James Jordan

Maine

MAINE

Number of Counties: 16

ANDROSCOGGIN

Phone: (207) 786-2421
Delinquent Property Tax Division
45 Spring St.
Auburn, ME 04210
Diane Fleve

AROOSTOOK

Phone: (207) 493-3318
Delinquent Property Tax Division
240 Sweden St., Suite 1
Caribou, ME 04736

CUMBERLAND

Phone: (207) 871-8380
Delinquent Property Tax Division
142 Federal St.
Portland, ME 04101-4196

FRANKLIN

Phone: (207) 778-6614
Delinquent Property Tax Division
38 Main St.
Farmington, ME 04938-1818

HANCOCK

Phone: (207) 667-8272
Delinquent Property Tax Division
60 State St.
Ellsworth, ME 04605
Robert Likin

KENNEBEC

Phone: (207) 287-4791
State House Station 24
Augusta, ME 04333

KNOX

Phone: (207) 594-0301
Delinquent Property Tax Division
62 Union St.
P.O. Box 546
Rockland, ME 04841

LINCOLN

Phone: (207) 882-6311
Delinquent Property Tax Division
P.O. Box 249
Wisacasset, ME 04578

OXFORD

Phone: (207) 743-6359
Delinquent Property Tax Division
P.O. Box 179
South Paris, ME 04281

PENOBSCOTT

Phone: (207) 942-8535
Delinquent Property Tax Division
97 Hammond St.
Bangor, ME 04401

SAGADAHOC

Phone: (207) 443-8200
Delinquent Property Tax Division
Sagadahoc County Courthouse
P.O. Box 246
Bath, ME 04530

SOMERSET

Phone: (207) 474-9861
Somerset County Courthouse
Delinquent Property Tax Division
Skowhegan, ME 04976

WALDO

Phone: (207) 338-3282
71 Church St.
Belfast, ME 04915

WASHINGTON

Phone: (207) 255-3127
Delinquent Property Tax Division
P.O. Box 297
Machias, ME 04654

YORK

Phone: (207) 324-1571
Delinquent Property Tax Division
Court St.
P.O. Box 399
Alfred, ME 04002

PISCATAQUIS

Phone: (207) 564-2161
Delinquent Property Tax Division
51 E. Main
Dover-Foxcroft, ME 04426

Minnesota

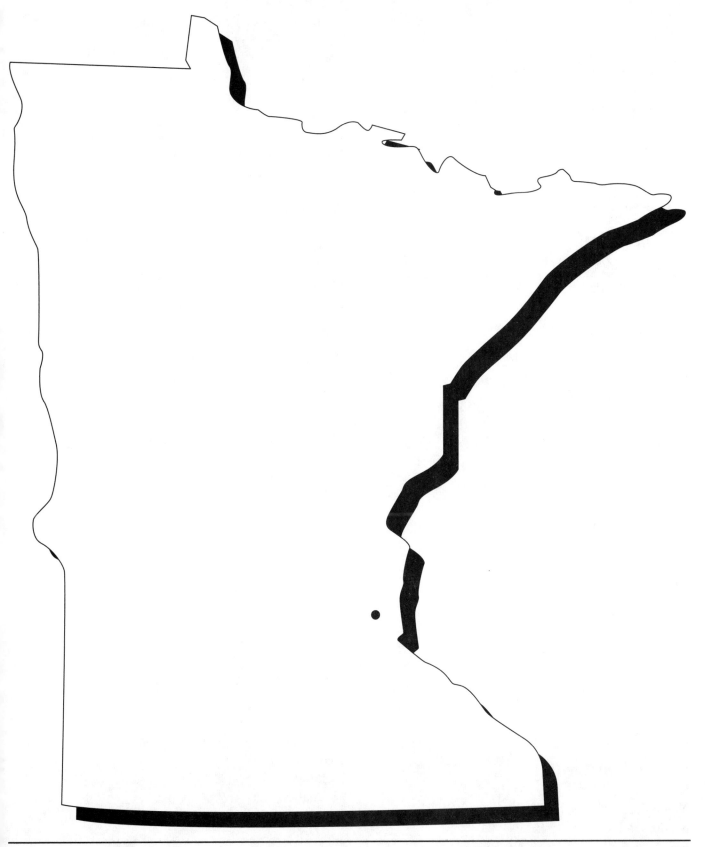

MINNESOTA

Number of Counties: 87

ANOKA

Phone: (612) 323-5442
Delinquent Property Tax Division
2100 3rd Ave.
Anoka, MN 55303

BECKER

Phone: (218) 846-7301
Delinquent Property Tax Division
P.O. Box 787
Detroit Lakes, MN 56502
Rita Thompson

BELTRAMI

Phone: (218) 759-4210
315 5th St. N.W.
Bemidji, MN 56601
Natural Resource Management

BENTON

Phone: (320) 968-6254
Delinquent Property Tax Division
P.O. Box 129
Foley, MN 56329
Joan Neyssen

BLUE EARTH

Phone: (507) 389-8100
David Twa
Land Records
P.O. Box 8608
Mankato, MN 56002-3567

BROWN

Phone: (507) 233-6616
P.O. Box 115
New Olm, MN 56073-0115
Marlon Helget

CARLTON

Phone: (218) 384-9125
Carlton County Courthouse
P.O. Box 160
Delinquent Property Tax Division
Carlton, MN 55718
Paul Gassert

CARVER

Phone: (612) 361-1980
Carver County Government Center
600 E. 4th St.
Chaska, MN 55318
Don Dahlke

CHICAGO

Phone: (612) 257-1300/1-888-234-1246
Delinquent Property Tax Division
313 N. Main St., Room 274
Center City, MN 55012
Lee Olson

CLAY

Phone: (218) 299-5011
807 N. 11th Street
Moorhead, MN 56560
Betty Swetland

CROW WING

Phone: (218) 828-3953
Delinquent Property Tax Division
326 Laurel St.
Brainerd, MN 56401-3590
Laureen Borden

DAKOTA

Phone: (612) 438-4418
Delinquent Property Tax Division
1590 Hwy 55 W.
Hastings, MN 55033
Thomas Novak

DOUGLAS

Phone: (320) 762-2381
Douglas County Courthouse
305 8th Ave. West
Alexandria, MN 56308-1793
Joyce Wieberdink

FREEBORN

Phone: (507) 377-5117
Delinquent Property Tax Division
P.O. Box 1147
Albert Lea, MN 56007-1147
Dennis Distad

GOODHUE

Phone: (612) 385-3038
P.O. Box 408
Red Wing, MN 55066
Jeff Cole

HENNEPIN

Phone: (612) 348-3734
Delinquent Property Tax Division
A600 Government Center
300 S. 6th St.
Minneapolis, MN 55487

ISANTI

Phone: (612) 689-1781
Delinquent Property Tax Division
555 18th Ave. SW
Cambridge, MN 55008
Lyle Myren

ITASCA

Phone: (218) 327-2859
123 NE 4th St.
Grand Rapids, MN 55744
Robert D. Cuehlke

KANDIYOHI

Phone: (612) 231-6225
P.O. Box 936
Willmar, MN 56201
Sam Modderman

LYON

Phone: (507) 537-6724
Delinquent Property Tax Division
607 W. Main St.
Marshall, MN 56258
Lisa Zmeskal

MARTIN

Phone: (507) 238-3219
Delinquent Property Tax Division
P.O. Box 208
Fairmont, MN 56031
Robert Katzenberger

MCLEOD

Phone: (320) 864-5551
830 E. 11th St. Suite 103
Glencoe, MN 55336
Linda Radtke

MORRISON

Phone: (612) 632-0151
Delinquent Property Tax Division
213 SE 1st Ave.
Little Falls, MN 56345
Rose Hubner

MOWER

Phone: (507) 437-9547
Delinquent Property Tax Division
201 1st St. NE
Austin, MN 55912
Ruth Harris

NICOLLET

Phone: (507) 931-6800
Delinquent Property Tax Division
P.O. Box 180
St. Peter, MN 56082
Merna Schoels

OLMSTEAD

Phone: (507) 285-8115
Delinquent Property Tax Division
51 4th St. SE
Rochester, MN 55902
Bob Ryan

OTTER TAIL

Phone: (218) 739-2271
County Auditor's Office
121 W. Junius Ave.
Fergus Falls, MN 56537-2586
Steve Andrews

POLK

Phone: (218) 281-2554
Delinquent Property Tax Division
612 N. Broadway, Suite 207
Crookston, MN 56716
Gerald Amiot

RAMSEY

Phone: (612) 266-2040
50 W. Kellogg Blvd., Suite 830
St. Paul, MN 55102
Genene Johnson

RICE

Phone: (507) 332-6104
Delinquent Property Tax Division
218 NW 3rd St.
Faribault, MN 55021
Lorainne Nelson

ST. LOUIS

Phone: (218) 726-2383
100 N. 5th Ave. W., Rm. 214
Duluth, MN 55802
Gordon D. McFaul

SCOTT

Phone: (612) 496-8150
Delinquent Property Tax Division
428 S. Holmes St.
Shakopee, MN 55379
Thomas Muelken

SHERBURNE

Phone: (612) 241-2590
Delinquent Property Tax Division
13880 Hwy. 10
Elk River, MN 55330-4607
Karen Hertel

STEARNS

Phone: (320) 656-3870
Delinquent Property Tax Division
Administration Center, Room 136
P.O. Box 728
St. Cloud, MN 56302-0728
Henry Kohorst

STELLE

Phone: (507) 444-7422
Delinquent Property Tax Division
P.O. Box 890
Owatonna, MN 55060
Steven Rohlik

TODD

Phone: (320) 732-4471
215 1st Ave. S
Long Prairie, MN 56347
Cathryn Gresser

WASHINGTON

Phone: (612) 430-6175
Washington County Auditor Office
P.O. Box 200
Stillwater, MN 55082
R.H. Stafford

WINONA

Phone: (507) 457-6350
Delinquent Property Tax Division
171 W. 3rd St.
Winona, MN 55987
Cheri MacLennan

WRIGHT

Phone: (612) 682-7574
Delinquent Property Tax Division
10 NW 2nd St., Room 232
Darla M. Groshems

AITKIN

Phone: (218) 927-7325
County Land Department
209 2nd St. N.W.
Aitkin, MN 56431
Vernon Nelson

BIG STONE

Phone: (320) 839-3445
20 SE 2nd St.
Ortonville, MN 56278
Cindy Nelson

CASS

Phone: (218) 547-3300
Delinquent Property Tax Division
P.O. Box 3000
Walker, MN 56484
Marge L. Daniels

CHIPPEWA

Phone: (320) 269-7447
629 N. 11st St.
Montevideo, MN 56265
Jon Clauson

CLEARWATER

Phone: (218) 694-6130
213 Main Ave. N.
Delinquent Property Tax Division
Bagley, MN 56621
Charlene Olson

COOK

Phone: (218) 387-3000
Delinquent Property Tax Division
P.O. Box 1150
Grand Mareis, MN 55604
Carol Gresczyk

COTTONWOOD

Phone: (507) 831-1905
Delinquent Property Tax Division
900 3rd Ave.
Windom, MN 56101
Jan Johnson

DODGE

Phone: (507) 635-6230
Delinquent Property Tax Division
P.O. Box 38
Manterville, MN 55955
Scott Umsted

FARIBAULT

Phone: (507) 526-6260
Delinquent Property Tax Division
P.O. Box 130
Blue Earth, MN 56013
Dave Frank

FILLMORE

Phone: (507) 765-3811
P.O. Box 627
Delinquent Property Tax Division
Preston, MN 55965
Angela D. Burrs

GRANT

Phone: (218) 685-4655
Delinquent Property Tax Division
10 2nd St. NE
Elbow Lake, MN 56531
Patricia A. Soberg

HOUSTON

Phone: (507) 724-5815
Delinquent Property Tax Division
304 S. Marshall
Caledonia, MN 55921
Audrey Petersen

HUBBARD

Phone: (218) 732-4348
301 Court Ave.
Park Rapids, MN 56470
Karen Sells

JACKSON

Phone: (507) 847-2763
405 4th St.
Courthouse
Jackson, MN 56143
Luther Glaser

KANABEC

Phone: (320) 679-1951
18 N. Vine St.
Mora, MN 55051
Mason Hjelle

KITTSON

Phone: (218) 843-3432
Delinquent Property Tax Division
410 S. 5th St.
P.O. Box 609
Hallock, MN 56728
Bob Laude

KOOCHICHING

Phone: (218) 283-6210
Delinquent Property Tax Division
715 4th St.
International Falls, MN 56649
Aaron Carew

LAC QUI PARLE

Phone: (320) 598-3648
Delinquent Property Tax Division
600 6th St.
Madison, MN 56256
Marlene Johnson

LAKE

Phone: (218) 834-8343
601 3rd Ave.
Two Harbors, MN 55616
Steve McMahon

LAKE OF THE WOODS

Phone: (218) 634-2361
Delinquent Property Tax Division
P.O. Box 808
Baudette, MN 56623
Mark Hall

LE SUEUR

Phone: (507) 357-8282
Delinquent Property Tax Division
88 Park Ave. South
Le Center, MN 56057
oseph Boettcher

LINCOLN

Phone: (507) 694-1522
Delinquent Property Tax Division
P.O. Box D
Ivanhoe, MN 56142
Mark Leibfried

MAHNOMEN

Phone: (218) 935-2545
Delinquent Property Tax Division
P.O. Box 400
Mahnomen, MN 56557
Dan Cook

MARSHALL

Phone: (218) 745-4851
Delinquent Property Tax Division
208 E. Colvin Ave.
Warren, MN 56762
Roy Swanson

MEEKER

Phone: (320) 693-5345
Delinquent Property Tax Division
325 Sibly Ave. N.
Litchfield, MN 55355
Allan Knutson

MILLE LACS

Phone: (612) 983-8301
635 2nd St. SE
Milaca, MN 56353
Phillip Thompson

MURRAY

Phone: (507) 836-6163
Delinquent Property Tax Division
P.O. Box 57
Slayton, MN 56172
Gary Spaeth

NOBLES

Phone: (507) 372-8231
Delinquent Property Tax Division
P.O. Box 757
Worthington, MN 56187
Sharon Balster

NORMAN

Phone: (218) 784-2101
Delinquent Property Tax Division
16 E. 3rd Ave.
Ada, MN 56510
Richard Munter

PENNINGTON

Phone: (218) 681-4011
Delinquent Property Tax Division
P.O. Box 616
101 Main Ave. N.
Thief River Falls, MN 56701
Kenneth Olson

PINE

Phone: (320) 245-2819
Pine County Land Dept.
P.O. Box 654
Sandstone, MN 55072
Greg Beck

PINESTONE

Phone: (507) 825-4494
Delinquent Property Tax Division
416 S. Hiawatha Ave.
Pipestone, MN 56164
Steve Ewing

POPE

Phone: (320) 634-5706
Delinquent Property Tax Division
130 E. Minesota Ave.
Glenwood, MN 56334
Mary Pischke

RED LAKE

Phone: (218) 637-2797
Delinquent Property Tax Division
P.O. Box 208
Red Lake Falls, MN 56750
ay Guillemette

REDWOOD

Phone: (320) 637-4013
Delinquent Property Tax Division
P.O. Box 130
Redwood Falls, MN 56283
Larry Bunting

RENVILLE

Phone: (320) 523-1172
Delinquent Property Tax Division
500 E. DePue
Olivia, MN 56277
Doug Knutson

ROCK

Phone: (507) 283-5060
Delinquent Property Tax Division
P.O. Box 509
Luverne, MI 56156
Margaret Cook

ROSEAU

Phone: (218) 463-1215
Delinquent Property Tax Division
06 5th Ave., SW, Rm. 140
Roseau, MN 56751
Diane Gregerson

SIBLEY

Phone: (507) 237-2820
Delinquent Property Tax Division
P.O. Box 51
400 Court
Gaylord, MN 55334
Wally Reckdahl

STEVENS

Phone: (612) 589-7418
Delinquent Property Tax Division
P.O. Box 530
Morris, MN 56267
Dick Bluth

SWIFT

Phone: (320) 843-3544
Delinquent Property Tax Division
P.O. Box 50
Benson, MN 56215
Byron Vadnaia

TRAVERSE

Phone: (320) 563-4616
Delinquent Property Tax Division
702 2nd Ave. N.
Wheaton, MN 56296
Allan Weick

WABASHA

Phone: (612) 565-4410
Delinquent Property Tax Division
625 Jefferson Ave.
Wabasha, MN 55981
William Pfeilsticker

WADENA

Phone: (218) 631-2629
Delinquent Property Tax Division
415 S. Jefferson
Wadena, MN 56482
L.G. Durkee

WASECA

Phone: (507) 835-0620
Delinquent Property Tax Division
P.O. Box 47e St.
Waseca, MN 56093
Pat Loeffler

WATONWAN

Phone: (507) 375-12133341
Delinquent Property Tax Division
P.O. Box 518
St. James, MN 56093
Carol Johnson

WILKIN

Phone: (218) 643-5112
Delinquent Property Tax Division
P.O. Box 368
Breckinridge, MN 56520
Rose Ann Hulne

YELLOW MEDICINE

Phone: (612) 564-3231
Delinquent Property Tax Division
415 9th Ave.
Granite Falls, MN 56241
Sharon Schuler

Nevada

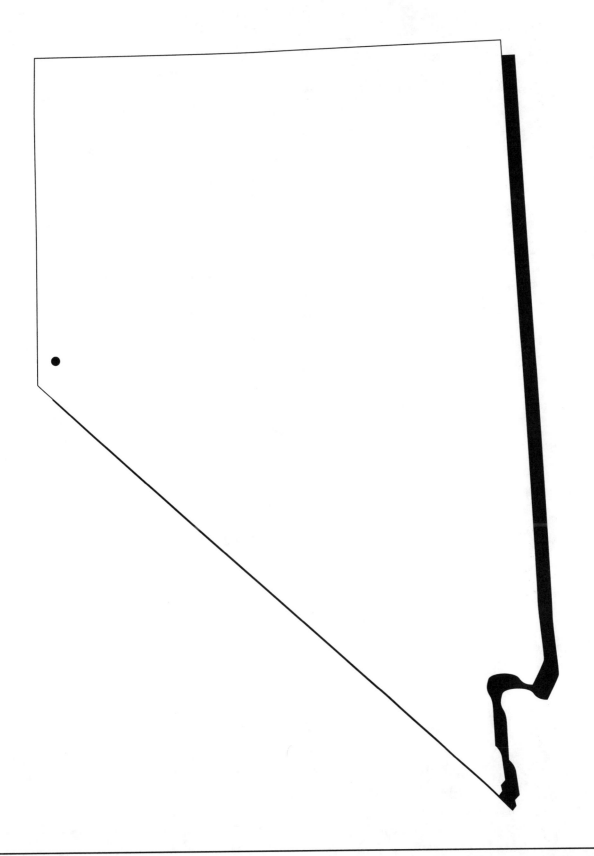

NEVADA

Number of Counties: 17

CHURCHILL

Phone: (702) 423-6028
10 W. Williams Ave.
Fallon, NV 89406
Gloria Venturacci

ESMERADLA

Phone: (702) 485-6309
Delinquent Property Tax Division
P.O. Box 547
Goldfield, NV 89013
Lyn Scott

EUREKA

Phone: (702) 237-5262
Delinquent Property Tax Division
P.O. Box 677
Eureka, NV 89316
Joan Shangle

HUMBOLDT

Phone: (702) 623-6445
50 W. Fifth Street
Winnemucca, NV 89445
Belle Bundy

LANDER

Phone: (702) 635-5127
Delinquent Property Tax Division
315 S. Humboldt
Battle Mountain, NV 89820
Grace Powrie

LINCOLN

Phone: (702) 962-5805
Delinquent Property Tax Division
P.O. Box 416
Pioche, NV 89043
Ruby Lister

LYON

Phone: (702) 463-6502
P.O. Box 816
Yerington, NV 89447
Marina Pinkerton

MINERAL

Phone: (702) 945-2446
Delinquent Property Tax Division
P.O. Box 1450
Hawthorne, NV 89415
Jean Justus

NYE

Phone: (702) 482-8194
P.O. Box 473
Tonopah, NV 89049
Patricia Foster

PERSHING

Phone: (702) 273-2208
Delinquent Property Tax Division
P.O. Box 820
Lovelock, NV 89419
Donna Giles

STOREY

Phone: (702) 847-0969
Delinquent Property Tax Division
P.O. Drawer D
Virginia City, NV 89440
Doreen Bacus

WHITE PINE

Phone: (702) 289-2341
Delinquent Property Tax Division
P.O. Box 1002
Ely, NV 89301
Beverly Cornutt

CARSON CITY

Phone: (702) 887-2095
2621 Northgate Lane, #11
Carson City, NV 89706
Alvin Kramer (702) 887-2082 Clerk

CLARK

Phone: (702) 455-4323
Delinquent Property Tax Division
Clark County Government Center
500 S. Grand Central Pkwy.
Las Vegas, NV 89155-1220
Mark Aston

DOUGLAS

Phone: (702) 782-9017
Delinquent Property Tax Division
P.O. Box 218
Minden, NV 89423
Barbara Reed

ELKO

Phone: (702) 738-5694
Treasurer
571 Idaho St., Suite 101
Elko, NV 89801
Ceasar Salicchi

WASHOE

Phone: (702) 328-2510
Delinquent Property Tax Division
P.O. Box 30039
Reno, NV 89520
Bill Berrum

New Mexico

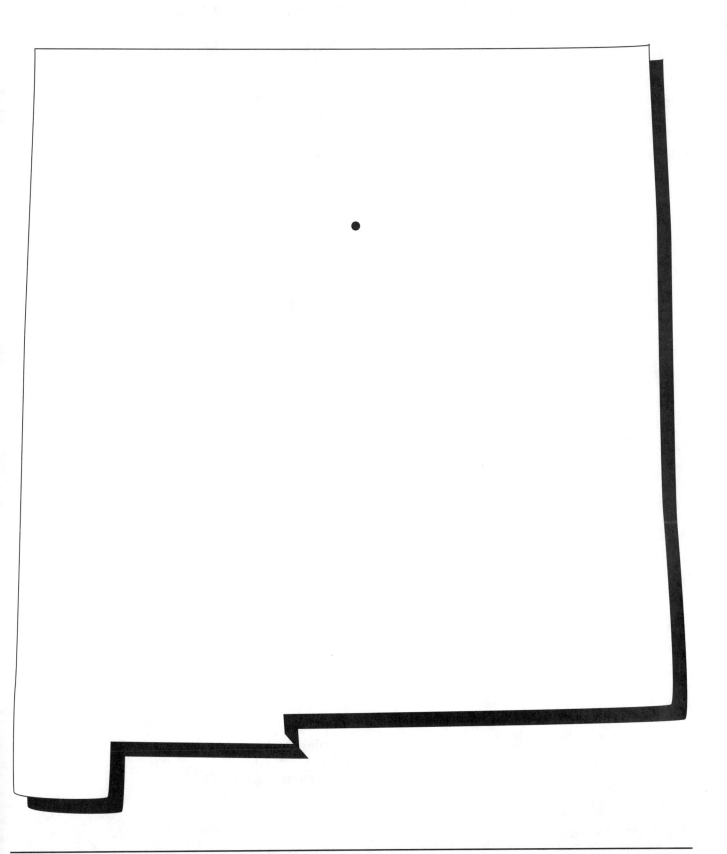

NEW MEXICO

BERNALILLO COUNTY CLERK
One Civic Plaza NW
Albuerque, NM 87102
(505) 768-4090
FAX (505) 768-4631

CATROO COUNTY CLERK
Box 197
Reserve, NM 87830
(505) 533-6400
FAX (505) 533-6400

CHAVES COUNTY CLERK
515 East High
Grants, NM 87020
(505) 287-8107
FAX (505) 285-5434

CIBOLA COUNTY CLERK
515 East High
Grants, NM 87020
(505) 287-8107
FAX (505) 285-5434

COLFAX COUNTY CLERK
Box 159
Raton, NM 87740
(505) 445-5551
FAX (505) 445-4031

CURRY COUNTY CLERK
Box 1168
Clovis, NM 88181
(505) 763-5591
FAX (505) 763-4232

DEBACA COUNTY CLERK
Box 347
Fort Sumner, NM 88119
(505) 355-2601
FAX (505) 355-2441

DONA ANA COUNTY CLERK
Courthouse
251 Amador Rm 103
Las Cruces, NM 88005
(505) 525-6659
FAX (505) 647-7464

EDDY COUNTY CLERK
Box 850
Carlsbad, NM 88221
(505) 885-3383
FAX (505) 887-1039

GUADALUPE COUNTY CLERK
420 Parker Avenue
Santa Rosa, NM 88435
(505) 472-3791
FAX (505) 472-3735

HARDING COUNTY CLERK
Box 1002
Mosquero, NM 87733
(505) 673-2301
FAX (505) 673-2922

HIDALGO COUNTY CLERK
300 S. Shakespeare
Lordsburg, NM 88495
(505) 542-9213
FAX (505) 542-3414

LEA COUNTY CLERK
Box 1507
Lovington, NM 88260
(505) 396-8521
FAX (505) 396-5684

LINCOLN COUNTY CLERK
Box 338
Carrizbzo, NM 88301
(505) 396-2384
FAX (505) 396-5684

LOS ALAMOS COUNTY CLERK
Box 30
Los Alamos, NM 87544
(505) 662-8010
FAX (505) 662-8008

LUNA COUNTY CLERK
Box 1838
Deming, NM 88031
(505) 546-0491
FAX (505) 546-4708

MCKINLEY COUNTY CLERK
Box 1268
Gallup, NM 87305
(505) 863-6866
FAX (505) 863-1419

MORA COUNTY CLERK
Box 360
Mora, NM 87732
(505) 387-2448
FAX (505) 387-9023

OTERO COUNTY CLERK
Box 780, 1000 New York Ave., Rm 108
Alamogordo, NM 88310
(505) 437-4942
FAX (505) 434-2509

QUAY COUNTY CLERK
Box 1225
Tucumcari, NM 88401
(505) 461-0510
FAX (505) 461-0513

RIO ARRIBA COUNTY CLERK
Box 158
Tierra Amarilla, NM 87575
(505) 588-7724
FAX (505) 588-7418

ROOSEVELT COUNTY CLERK
Courthouse
Portales, NM 88130
(505) 356-8562
FAX (505) 356-3560

SANDOVAL COUNTY CLERK
Box 40
Bernalillo, NM 87004
(505) 867-7572
FAX (505) 771-8610

SAN JUAN COUNTY CLERK
Box 550
Aztec, NM 87410
(505) 334-9471
FAX (505) 334-3635

SAN MIGUEL COUNTY CLERK
Courthouse
Las Vegas, NM 87701
(505) 425-9331
FAX (505) 454-1799

SANTA FE COUNTY CLERK
Box 1985
Santa Fe, NM 87504
(505) 986-6281
FAX (505) 986-6206

SIERRA COUNTY CLERK
311 Date St.
Truth or Consequences, NM 87901
(505) 894-2840
FAX (505) 894-2516

SOCORRO COUNTY CLERK
Box 1
Socorro, NM 87801
(505) 835-0423
FAX (505) 835-1043

TAOS COUNTY CLERK
105 Albright
Taos, NM 87571
(505) 758-8836
FAX (505) 751-3391

TORRANCE COUNTY CLERK
Box 48
Estancia, NM 87016
(505) 384-2221

UNION COUNTY CLERK
Box 430
Clayton, NM 88415
(505) 374-9491
FAX (505) 374-2763

VALENCIA COUNTY CLERK
Box 969
Los Lunas, NM 87031
(505) 866-2073 Ext. 43
FAX (505) 866-2023

THIS PAGE INTENTIONALLY LEFT BLANK FOR NOTES

Ohio

OHIO

Number of Counties: 86

ADAMS

Phone: (513) 544-2317
Delinquent Property Tax Division
110 W. Main St.
West Union, OH 45693
Howard Harris

ALLEN

Phone: (419) 228-3700
Delinquent Property Tax Division
P.O. Box 123
Lima, OH 45802
Richard Ditto

ASHLAND

Phone: (419) 289-0000
Delinquent Property Tax Division
Ashland County Courthouse
West 2nd Street
Ashland, OH 44805
Cindy Funk

ASHTABULA

Phone: (216) 576-3729
25 W. Jefferson St.
Jefferson, OH 44047
Robert L. Harvey

ATHENS

Phone: (614) 592-3231
Delinquent Property Tax Division
15 S. Court St.
Athens, OH 45701
JaVon Kittle Cooper

AUGLAIZE

Phone: (419) 738-2510
Delinquent Property Tax Division
P.O. Box 56
Wapakoneta, OH 45895
Genevie Pitchford

BELMONT

Phone: (614) 695-2121
Delinquent Property Tax Division
Main Street Courthouse
St. Clairsville, OH 43950
Joseph A. Gaudio

BROWN

Phone: (513) 378-6705
Delinquent Property Tax Division
800 Mt. Orab Pike
Georgetown, OH 45121
Gail DeClaire

BUTLER

Phone: (513) 887-3000
Delinquent Property Tax Division
130 High Street
Hamilton, OH 45011
Mary C. Law

CARROLL

Phone: (216) 627-2250
Delinquent Property Tax Division
119 Public Square
Carrollton, OH 44615-1495
John Yeager

CHAMPAIGN

Phone: (513) 653-4836
Delinquent Property Tax Division
214 N. Main
Urbana, OH 43078
J.A. Underwood

CLARK

Phone: (513) 328-2432
P.O. Box 1305
Springfield, OH 45501
Steven Metzger

CLERMONT

Phone: (513) 732-7254
Delinquent Property Tax Division
101 E. Main
Batavia, OH 45103
J. Robert True

CLINTON

Phone: (513) 382-2224
Delinquent Property Tax Division
46 S. South St.
Wilmington, OH 45177
Joyce Attey

COLUMBIANA

Phone: (216) 424-9511
Delinquent Property Tax Division
105 S. Market St.
P.O. Box 469
Lisbon, OH 44432
Angeline Frank

COSHOCTON

Phone: (614) 622-2731
349 Main St.
Coschocton, OH 43812
Michelle Darner

CRAWFORD

Phone: (419) 562-7861
Delinquent Property Tax Division
P.O. Box 565
Bucyrus, OH 44820
Glen Cole

CUYAHOGA

Phone: (216) 443-7000
Delinquent Property Tax Division
1219 Ontario St.
Cleveland, OH 44113
Francis Gaul

DARKE

Phone: (513) 547-7370
Delinquent Property Tax Division
Darke County Courthouse, 1st Floor
Greenville, OH 45331
Scott J. Zumbrink

DEFIANCE

Phone: (419) 782-4761
Delinquent Property Tax Division
221 Clinton St.
Defiance, OH 43512
Karen Tubbs

DELAWARE

Phone: (614) 368-1800
Delinquent Property Tax Division
91 N. Sandusky
Delaware, OH 43015-1799
Dale M. Wilgus

ERIE

Phone: (419) 627-7673
Delinquent Property Tax Division
247 Columbus Ave., Suite 115
Sandusky, OH 44870
Beverly Pressler

FAIRFIELD

Phone: (614) 687-7190
Delinquent Property Tax Division
210 E. Main, Rm. 203
Lancaster, OH 43130
Jon A. Slater, Jr.

FRANKLIN

Phone: (614) 462-3000
Delinquent Property Tax Division
373 S. High St., 17th Floor
Columbus, OH 43215
Bobby M. Hall

FULTON

Phone: (419) 337-9252
Delinquent Property Tax Division
210 S. Fulton
Wauseon, OH 43567
Dennis Hales

GALLIA

Phone: (614) 446-4612
Delinquent Property Tax Division
18 Locust St., Rm. 1291
Gallipolis, OH 45631
Larry Betz

GEAUGA

Phone: (216) 285-2222, ext. 5920
Delinquent Property Tax Division
231 Main St.
Chardon, OH 44024
George W. Taylor

GREENE

Phone: (513) 376-5000
Delinquent Property Tax Division
P.O. Box 427
Xenia, OH 45385
James W. Schmidt
GUERNSEY

Phone: (614) 432-9200
Delinquent Property Tax Division
801 Wheeling Ave.
Cambridge, OH 43725
Jim Caldwell

HAMILTON

Phone: (513) 632-6500
Delinquent Property Tax Division
138 E. Court St., Rm. 402
Cincinnati, OH 45202
Robert A. Goering

HANCOCK

Phone: (419) 424-7214
Delinquent Property Tax Division
300 S. Main St.
Findlay, OH 45840
J.R. Brondes

HARDIN

Phone: (419) 674-2205
Delinquent Property Tax Division
One Courthouse Sq., Suite 230
Kenton ,OH 43326
Ruth Ann Cook

HENRY

Phone: (419) 592-1851
Delinquent Property Tax Division
P.O. Box 546
Napoleon, OH 43545
Calvin Spiess

HIGHLAND

Phone: (513) 393-9951
Delinquent Property Tax Division
P.O. Box 824
Hillsboro, OH 45133
Ann Williams

HOCKING

Phone: (513) 393-9951
Delinquent Property Tax Division
P.O. Box 28
Logan, OH 43138
Dorothy Rafferty

HOLMES

Phone: (216) 674-5871
Delinquent Property Tax Division
34 D. South City
Millersburg, OH 44654
Joyce Yoder

HURON

Phone: (419) 668-2090
Delinquent Property Tax Division
5 East Main
Norwalk, OH 44857
Ardeth Chupp

JACKSON

Phone: (614) 286-2402
Delinquent Property Tax Division
226 Main St.
Jackson, OH 45640
Tim Coll

JEFFERSON

Phone: (614) 283-8572
Delinquent Property Tax Division
P.O. Box 398
Steubenville, OH 43952
Raymond Agresta

KNOX

Phone: (614) 393-6735
106 E. High St.
Mount Vernon, OH 43050
Betty J. Beckley

LAKE

Phone: (216) 350-2516
Delinquent Property Tax Division
P.O. Box 490
Painesville, OH 44077
John Crocker

LAWRENCE

Phone: (614) 533-4300
Delinquent Property Tax Division
Veteran's Square
Ironton, OH 45638
Kenneth C. Howell

LICKING

Phone: (614) 349-6000
Delinquent Property Tax Division
20 S. 2nd St.
Newark, OH 43055
J. Terry Evans

LOGAN

Phone: (513) 599-7283
Delinquent Property Tax Division
100 S. Madriver, Rm. 104
Bellefontaine, OH 43311
Joy King

LORAIN

Phone: (216) 329-5000
Delinquent Property Tax Division
226 Middle Ave.
Elyria, OH 44035
Daniel J. Talarek

LUCAS

Phone: (419) 245-4301
One Government Center, Suite 670
Toledo, OH 43604
Ray Kest

MADISON

Phone: (614) 852-1936
Delinquent Property Tax Division
P.O. Box 675
London, OH 43140
William Stidham

MAHONING

Phone: (216) 740-2130
Delinquent Property Tax Division
120 Market St.
Youngstown, OH 44503
George McKelvey

MARION

Phone: (614) 387-5871
Delinquent Property Tax Division
One Courthouse Square
Marion, OH 43302
Thomas Sheskey

MEDINA

Phone: (216) 723-3641
Delinquent Property Tax Division
144 N. Broadway
Medina, OH 44256
John A. Burke

MERCER

Phone: (419) 586-3178
Delinquent Property Tax Division
101 N. Main St., Rm. 201
Celina, OH 45822
Robert C. King

MIAMI

Phone: (513) 332-6800
Delinquent Property Tax Division
201 W. Main St.
Troy, OH 45373
Lydia Callison
MONTGOMERY

Phone: (513) 225-4690
451 W. 3rd St.
P.O. Box 972
Dayton, OH 45422
Hugh Quill

MORROW

Phone: (419) 947-6070
Delinquent Property Tax Division
48 E. High St.
Mount Gilead, OH 43338
Randall Webber

MUSKINGUM

Phone: (614) 455-7118
Delinquent Property Tax Division
401 Main St.
Zanesville, OH 43701
George W. Roll

OTTAWA

Phone: (419) 734-6710
Delinquent Property Tax Division
315 Madison St., Rm. 201
Port Clinton, OH 43452
Jaque Chapman

PERRY

Phone: (614) 342-1235
Delinquent Property Tax Division
P.O. Box 288
New Lexington, OH 43764
David R. Wilson

PICKAWAY

Phone: (614) 474-6093
Delinquent Property Tax Division
2075 Court St., Rm. 2
Circleville, OH 43113
Beverly K. Crawford

PORTAGE

Phone: (216) 297-3600
Delinquent Property Tax Division
449 S. Meridian St.
Ravenna, OH 44266
Maureen Frederick

PREBLE

Phone: (513) 456-8143
Delinquent Property Tax Division
2nd Floor Courthouse
Eaton, OH 45320
Barbara Suggs

PUTNAM

Phone: (419) 523-6588
Delinquent Property Tax Division
245 E. Main St., Suite 203
Ottawa, OH 45875-1960
Jean Quinn

RICHLAND

Phone: (419) 774-5550
Delinquent Property Tax Division
50 Park Ave. E
Mansfield, OH 44902
Daniel F. Smith

ROSS

Phone: (614) 775-7370
Delinquent Property Tax Division
Ross County Courthouse
2 N. Pain St.
Chillicothe, OH 45601
Felix Melaragno

SANDUSKY

Phone: (419) 334-6234
Delinquent Property Tax Division
100 N. Park Ave.
Fremont, OH 43420
Virgil Swartzlander

SCIOTO

Phone: (614) 355-8313
Delinquent Property Tax Division
602 7th St., Rm. 102
Portsmouth, OH 45662
Margaret Gordley

SENECA

Phone: (419) 447-1584
103 S. Washington St.
Tiffin, OH 44883
Marguerite O. Bernard

SHELBY

Phone: (513) 498-7281
Delinquent Property Tax Division
129 E. Court St.
Sidney, OH 45365
Mary Ellen Allenbaugh

STARK

Phone: (216) 438-0814
Delinquent Property Tax Division
200 W. Tuscarawas St.
Canton, OH 44702
Mark Roach

SUMMIT

Phone: (216) 643-2500
Delinquent Property Tax Division
175 S. Main St.
Akron, OH 44308
John A. Donofrio

TRUMBULL

Phone: (216) 675-2436
Delinquent Property Tax Division
160 High St.
Warren, OH 44481
Chris Michelakis

TUSCARAWAS

Phone: (216) 364-8811
Delinquent Property Tax Division
P.O. Box 250
New Philadelphia, OH 44663
Don W. Levengood

UNION

Phone: (513) 645-3035
Delinquent Property Tax Division
P.O. Box 420
Marysville, OH 43040-0420
Tamara K. Lowe

VAN WERT

Phone: (419) 238-5177
Delinquent Property Tax Division
Van Wert County Courthouse
121 E. Main St.
Van Wert, OH 45891
Harold Merkle

WARREN

Phone: (513) 932-4040
Delinquent Property Tax Division
320 E. Silver St.
Lebanon, OH 45036
Cicero Feltner

WASHINGTON

Phone: (614) 373-6623
Delinquent Property Tax Division
Courthouse
Marietta, OH 45750
Dorothy K. Peppel

WAYNE

Phone: (216) 287-5400
428 W. Liberty St.
Wooster, OH 44691
Jo Ann Spigelmire

WILLIAMS

Phone: (419) 636-1850
Delinquent Property Tax Division
1 Courthouse Square
Bryan, OH 43506
Elaine Willibey

HARRISON

Phone: (614) 942-8861
Delinquent Property Tax Division
100 W. Market
Cadiz, OH 43907
George Campbell

MEIGS

Phone: (614) 992-2004
P.O. Box 231
Pomeroy, OH 45769
Howard E. Frank

MONROE

Phone: (614) 472-1341
Delinquent Property Tax Division
101 N. Main
Woodsfield, OH 43793
Judy Gramlich

MORGAN

Phone: (614) 962-3561
Delinquent Property Tax Division
19 E. Main St.
McConnelsville, OH 43756
Kaye Tatman

NOBLE

Phone: (614) 732-2969
Delinquent Property Tax Division
Noble County Courthouse
290 Courthouse Square
Caldwell, OH 43724
Becky Hendershot

PAULDING

Phone: (419) 399-8280
Delinquent Property Tax Division
Paulding County Courthouse
115 N. Williams
Paulding, OH 45879
Betty Layman

PIKE

Phone: (614) 947-4817
Delinquent Property Tax Division
100 E. 2nd St.
Waverly, OH 45690
Donald E. Davis

VINTON

Phone: (614) 596-4571
Delinquent Property Tax Division
Vinton County Courthouse
McArthur, OH 45651
Larry Clary

WYANDOT

Phone: (419) 294-2131
Delinquent Property Tax Division
Wyandot County Courthouse
109 S. Sandusky Ave.
Upper Sandusky, OH 43351
Eugene Chaney

THIS PAGE INTENTIONALLY LEFT BLANK FOR NOTES

Oklahoma

OKLAHOMA

ADAIR

Adair Co. Courthouse
Stillwell, OK 74960
(918) 696-7551
(918) 696-7551
Janice Breurer

ALFALFA

300 S. Grand
Cherokee, OK 73728
(405) 596-3148
(405) 596-2254
Troy Koehen

ATOKA

200 East Court
Atoka, OK
(405) 889-5283
Richard Lillard

BEAVER

P.O. Box 249
Beaver, OK 73932
(405) 625-3161
(405) 625-3430
Jim Stafford

BECKHAM

P.O. Box 600
Sayre, OK 73662
(405) 928-2589
Karletta Bilbrey

BLAINE

P,O. Box 140
Watonga, OK
(405) 623-5007
(405) 623-5009
Carol Lynn Foley

BRYAN

402 W. Evergreen
Durant, OK
(405) 924-0748
(405) 924-3094
Sandra Mazzone

CADDO

P.O.Box 278
Anavarko, OK 73005
(405) 247-5151
John Cochran

CANADIAN

P.O. Box 1095
El Reno, OK
(405) 262-1070
(405) 422-2429
David Radcliff

CARTER

20 B Street, S.W., Rm. 104
Ardmore, OK 73401
(405) 223-9467
LaDonna Miller

CHEROKEE

213 W. Delaware , Rm. 207
Tahleguah,OK 74464
(918) 456-3321
Charlene Vance

CHOCTAW

300 E. Duke
Hugo,OK 74743
(405) 326-6142
Barbara Harmen

CIMARRON

P.O.Box 162
Boise City, OK 73933
(405) 544-2261
(405) 544-3420
Gkayla James

CLEVLAND

201 S. Jones
Norman,OK 73069
(405) 366-0217
(405) 366-0205
Carol Lowrey

COAL

4 N. Main St., Suite 4
Coalgate, OK 74538
(405) 927-3121
(405) 927-2438
Carol Denson

COMANCHE

315 S.W. 5th St.
Lawton, OK 73502
(405) 355-5763
(405) 357-9478
Inola Ash

COTTON

301 N. Broadway St.
Walters, OK 73502
(405) 875-3264
(405) 875-3756
Geneva Hawkins

CRAIG

P.O.Box 597
Vinita,OK 74301
(918) 256-2286
(918) 256-3617
Joan Barenett, Vinita Daily Journal
(918) 256-6422

CREEK

317 E. Lee, Rm. 201
Sapulpla,OK 74066-4342
(918) 224-4501
Bessa Hammontree
Sapulpa Hearld

CUSTER

P.O.Box 200
Arapaho, OK 73620
(405) 323-2292
(405) 323-2295
Karen Clonton

DELAWARE

P.O.Box 1080
Jay, OK 74346
(918) 253-4533
(918) 253-8707
Carole Rutherford, Delaware County Journal

DEWEY

P.O.Box 38
Taloga, OK 73667
(405) 328-5501
Cindy Farris, Taloga Times Advocate

ELLIS

P.O.Box 176
Arnett, OK
(405) 885-7675
(405) 885-7258
Cynthia Hunder

GARFIELD

114 W. Broadway, Rm. 104
Enid, OK 73701
(405) 237-0246
(405) 249-5951
Shirley Lorenz, Enid Morning News

GANIN

201 W. Grant
Pauls Valley, OK 73075
(405) 238-7301
Debbie Cornell

GRADY

P.O. Box 280
Chickasha,OK 73023
(405) 224-5337
(405) 222-4506
Rosalee Math
Chickasha Daily Express
(405) 224-2600

GRANT

P.O.Box 47
Medford, OK 73759
(405) 345-2284
(405) 395-2548
Jerry Dark

GREER

P.O.Box 478
Mangam, OK 73554
(405) 782-5515
Marguita Francis

HARMON

114 W. Hollis
Hollis, OK 73550
(405) 688-3566
Robbie Gee

HARPER

P.O.Box 440
Buffalo, OK
(405) 735-2442
Arlene Ahboah

HASKELL

P.O. Box 718
Stigler, OK 74462
(918) 967-2441
Gale Mitchell

HUGHES

200 N. Broadway
Holjenville, OK 74848
(405) 379-5371
Bobby Smith

JACKSON

101 N. Main
Altus, OK 73522
(405) 482-4371
Bonnie Shelton
Altus Times

JEFFERSON

220 N. Main, Rm. 104
Waurika, OK 73573-2235
(405) 228-2967
(405) 228-2029
Vickie Beherns
Ryan Leader

JOHNSTON

414 W. Main, Suite 103
Tishomingo, OK 73573-2235
(405)371-3082
Myrna McDonald
Johnston County Democrat

KAY

Kay Co. Courthouse
Newkirk, OK 74647
(405) 362-2523
(405) 362-3300
Pat Schieber
Newkirk Hearld Journal

KINGFISHER

101 S. Main
Kingfisher, OK 73750
(405) 375-3827
(405) 375-6033
Karen Mueggenborg

KIOWA

P.O.Box 900
Hobart, OK 73652
(405) 726-2362
Deanna Beamon
Mountain View News

LATIMER

109 N. Central
Wilberton, OK 74578
(918) 465-3450
Sue Chesder
New Tribune

LEFLORE

100 Broadway
Poteau, OK 74953
(918) 647-3525
(918) 647-8930
Stella Drury
Poteau Daily News & Sun

LINCOLN

811 Manuel Ave., Suite 6
Chandler, OK 74834
(495) 258-1491
(405) 258-1135
Robert James
Wellston News

LOGAN

P.O.Box 219
Guthrie, OK 73044
(405) 282-3154
(405) 282-6090
Guthrie Newsleader

LOVE

405 W. Main, Suite 204
Marietta, OK 73448
(405) 276-3260
Langdon Spivey
Marietta Monitor

MAJOR

P.O.Box 455
Fairview, OK 73737
(405) 227-4782
Reba Hiebert
Fairview Republican

MARSHALL

Marshall Co. Courthkouse
Madill, OK 73446
(405) 795-2463
Loyce Eldridge
Madill Record

MAYES

P.O.Box 9
Pryor, OK 74362
(918) 825-0160
(918) 825-2913
Martha Carmen
Daily Times

MC CLAIN

121 N. 2nd
Mc Clain Co. Courthouse
Purcell, OK 73080
(405) 527-3261
Twana Haley
Purcell Registar

MC CURTAIN

108 N. Central
Idabel, OK 74745
(405) 286-5128
(405) 286-7495
Joanne Strong
McCartin Gazette

MC INTOSH

P.O. Box 1547
Eufaula, OK 74432
(918) 689-2491
(918) 689-2620
Carol Lindley
Checotah Democrat

MURRAY

P.O.Box 304
Sulphur, OK 73086
(405) 622-5622
Barbara Woods
Sulphur Times Democrat

MUSKOGEE

P.O.Box 1587
Muskogee, OK 74402-1587
(918) 682-0811
Dorothy Lawson
Muskogee Phoenix

NOBLE

300 Courthouse Dr. #7
Perry, OK 73077
(405) 336-2026
Rita Howry
Perry Daily Journal

NOWATA

P.O. Box 427
Nowata, OK 74048
(918) 273-3562
Naydean Wesson

OTTAWA

P.O.Box 1024
Miami, OK 74355
(918) 542-8232
Brenda Conner
Miami News Record

OKFUSKEE

P.O.Box 308
Okemah, OK 74859
(918) 623-1494
(918) 623-0739
Dorothy Ross
Okemah News Leader

OKLAHOMA

320 Robert S. Kerr, Suite 307
Oklahoma, OK 73102
(405) 278-1300
(405) 278-7158
Forrest Butch Freeman

OKMULGEE

Okmulgee Co. Courthouse, Rm. 201
Okmulgee, OK 74447
(918) 756-3848
(918) 758-1202
Phyllis Stephens
Okmulgee Daily Times

OSAGE

P.O.Box 1569
Pawhuska, OK 74056
(918) 287-3101
Joyce Hathcort
Pawhuska Journal Capital

PAWNEE

500 Harrison, Rm. 200
Pawnee, OK 74058
(918) 762-2418
Anita Harris

PAWNEE CHIEF

Payne

P.O.Box 1597
Stillwater, OK 74076
(405) 624-9411
Bonita Stadler
Stillwater News Press

PITTSBURG

115 E. Carl Albert Pkwy
Mc Alester, OK 74501
(918) 423-6895
Johnnie Mac Griffin
News Capital

PONTOTOC

P.O.Box 1808
Ada, OK 74820
(405) 332-0183
(405) 436-5613
Thelma Hooper
Ada Evening News

POTTAWATOMIE

325 N. Broadway
Shawnee,OK 74801
(405) 273-0214
(405) 275-3516
Tammie Willis
County Democrat
(405) 273-8888

PUSHMATAHA

203 S.W. 3rd St.
Antlers, OK 74523
(405) 298-2580
Jenny Beth Caraway
Antler America
Clayton Today

ROGER MILLS

P.O.Box 340
Cheyenne, OK 73628
(405) 497-3349
(405) 497-3488
John L. Smith
Cheyenne Star

ROGERS

219 S. Missouri, Suite 101
Claremore, OK 74017
(918) 341-3159
(918) 342-3646
Kathy Baker
Claremore Progress

SEMINOLE

P.O. Box 1340
Wewoka, OK 74884
(405) 257-6262
Jim Hardin
Wewoka Daily Times
Seminole Producer

SEQUOYAH

P.O. Box 744
Sallisaw, OK 74955
(918) 775-9321
Martha Taylor
Swquoyah County Times

STEPHENS

101 S. 11th,, Rm. 207
Stephens Co. Courthouse
Duncan, OK73533
(405) 244-0728
(405) 252-5950
Sharon Mc Garr
Duncan Banner

TEXAS

P.O.Box 509
Guymon, OK 73942
(405) 338-7050
Rita Wise
Guymon Daily Hearld

TILLMAN

Box 986
TillmanCo. Courthouse
Frederick, OK 73542
(405) 335-3425
Kim Lamb
Frederick Leader

TULSA

500 S. Denver
Tulsa, OK 74103
(918) 596-5071
(918) 596-4695
Dennis Semler
Tulsa Daily Commerce &
Legal News

WAGNER

307 E. Cherokee
Wagnor, OK 74467
(918) 485-2149
Mary Sue Tedder
Wagnor Tribune

WASHINGTON

420 S. Johnstone
Bartlesville, OK 74003
(918) 337-2810
(918) 337-2891
Stan Stevens
Examiner Enterprize

WASHITA

P.O.Box 416
Cordell, OK 73632
(405) 832-2767
Ronald Piercy
Cordell Beacon

WOODS

P.O.Box 7
Alva, OK 73717
(405) 327-0308
(405) 327-6200
Barbara Long
Alva Review Currier

WOODWARD

P.O.Box 1007
Woodward, OK 73802
(405) 256-7404
(405) 254-6809
Mary Jane Hensley
Woodward News

GARVIN

201 W. Grant
Pauls Valley, OK 73075
(405) 238-7301
Debbie Cornell

Oregon

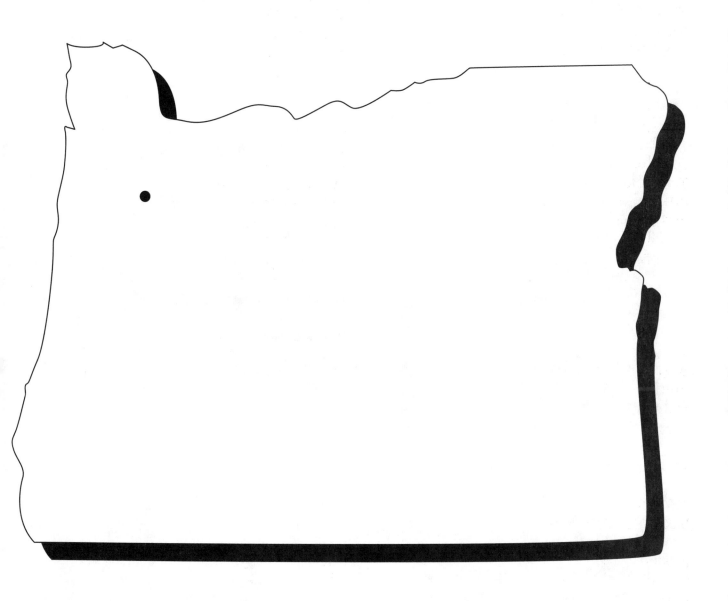

OREGON

Number of Counties: 34

BENTON

Phone: (503) 757-6808
Delinquent Property Tax Division
P.O. Box 964
Corvallis, OR 97339
Clark Ruggles

CLACKAMAS

Phone: (503) 655-8671
168 Warner Milney Rd.
Oregon City, OR 97045-1100
Ray Erland

CLATSOP

Phone: (503) 325-8522
Delinquent Property Tax Division
P.O. Box 177
Astoria, OR 97103
Glen Jones

COLUMBIA

Phone: (503) 397-2240
Columbia County Courthouse
St. Helens, OR 97051
Tom Linhers

COOS

(541) 756-2020, ext. 266
Coos County Assessor
250 N. Baxter
Coquille, OR 97423
Gayland VanElsberg

DESCHUTES

Phone: (503) 388-6508
Delinquent Property Tax Division
1164 Northwest Bond
Bend, OR 97701
Kim Worrell

DOUGLAS

Phone: (503) 440-4222
Douglas County Courthouse
1036 SE Douglas Ave.
Roseburg, OR 97470
Doris Reddekopp

JACKSON

Phone: (541) 776-7061
10 S. Oakdale
Medford, OR 97501
Nancy J. Wolf

KLAMATH

Phone: (503) 883-5111
Delinquent Property Tax Division
305 Main St.
Klamath Falls, OR 97601
Reg LeQuieu

LANE

Phone: (503) 687-4170
125 E. 8th Ave.
Eugene, OR 97401
Jim Gangle

LINCOLN

Phone: (503) 265-6611
Delinquent Property Tax Division
225 W. Olive, Rm. 205
Newport, OR 97365
Linda Pitzer

LINN

Phone: (503) 967-3825
P.O. Box 100
Albany, OR 97321
Mark Noakes

MARION

Phone: (503) 588-5215
Delinquent Property Tax Division
100 High St. NE
P.O. Box 2511
Salem, OR 97308
Ralph Grim

MULTNOMAH

Phone: (503) 248-3326
Delinquent Property Tax Division
1120 SW 5th Ave.
Portland, OR 97204

POLK

Phone: (503) 623-9264
Delinquent Property Tax Division
850 Main St.
Dallas, OR 97338
Carolyn Wall

UMATILLA

Phone: (503) 276-7111, ext. 217
216 SE 4th St.
P.O. Box 68
Pendleton, OR 97801
Rhonda Schultz

WASHINGTON

Phone: (503) 648-8801
155 N 1st Ave., Suite 130
Hillsboro, OR 97124
Debby Huggins

YAMHILL

Phone: (503) 472-9371
Delinquent Property Tax Division
535 E. 5th St.
McMinnville, OR 97128
Julia Staigers

OBAKER

Phone: (503) 523-8200
1995 Third St.
Baker City, OR 97814
Lynne Taylor

COOK

Phone: (541) 447-6554
Delinquent Property Tax Division
300 E. 3rd St.
Prineville, OR 97754
Mary J. Johnson

CURRY

Phone: (503) 247-7011, ext. 262
Commissioners Office
P.O. Box 746
Gold Beach, OR 97444
Trudy Stagn

GILLIAM

Phone: (503) 384-6321
Delinquent Property Tax Division
221 S. Oregon
P.O. Box 427
Condon, OR 97823

GRANT

Phone: (503) 575-0059
Delinquent Property Tax Division
P.O. Box 10
Canyon City, OR 97820
Lane Burton

HARNEY

Phone: (503) 573-8365
Delinquent Property Tax Division
450 N. Buena Vista
Burnes, OR 97720
Hunter Depue

HOOD RIVER

Phone: (503) 386-3970
Delinquent Property Tax Division
309 State St.
Hood River, OR 97031-2093

JEFFERSON

Phone: (503) 475-2449
Delinquent Property Tax Division
Jefferson County Courthouse
Maddras, OR 97741

LAKE

Phone: (503) 947-6000
Lake County Courthouse
513 Center
Lakeview, OR 97630
Phil Isreal

MORROW

Phone: (503) 676-9061
P.O. Box 279
Heppner, OR 97836
Marilyn Childers

SHERMAN

Phone: (503) 565-3623
Delinquent Property Tax Division
P.O. Box 424
Moro, OR 97039
Shirley MacAllister

TILLAMOOK

Phone: (503) 842-3403
Commissioners Office
201 Laurel Ave.
Tillamock, OR 97141
Sharon Hightower

UNION

Phone: (503) 963-1001
1100 L Ave.
LaGrande, OR 97850

WALLOWA

Phone: (503) 426-4543
Delinquent Property Tax Division
101 S. River St., Rm. 103
Enterprise, OR 97828
Ernestine Kilgore

WASCO

Phone: (503) 296-2207
Delinquent Property Tax Division
County Courthouse, 5th & Washington
The Dalles, OR 97058

WHEELER

Phone: (503) 763-2400
Delinquent Property Tax Division
P.O. Box 345
Fossil, OR 97830
Nancy Misener

Pennsylvania

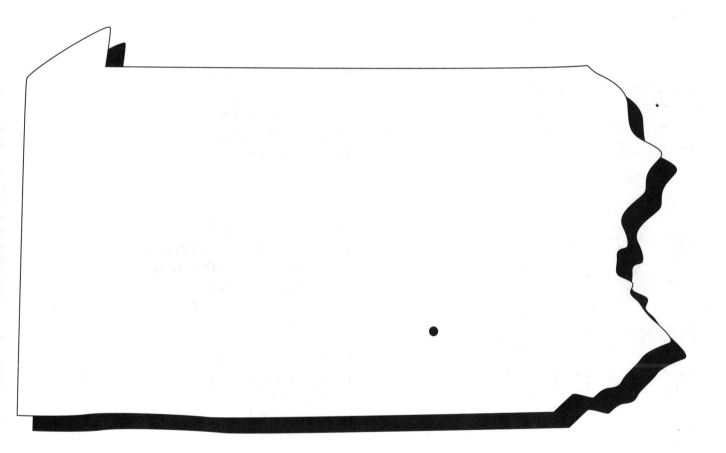

PENNSYLVANIA

Number of Counties: 64

ADAMS

Phone: (717) 334-6781
Delinquent Property Tax Division
 P.O. Box 3181
Gettysburg, PA 17325
Danielle Asper

ALLEGHENY

Phone: (412) 350-4101
Delinquent Property Tax Division
Allegheny County Courthouse, Rm. 108
436 Grand St.
Pittsburgh, PA 15219
Mary Alice McDonough

ARMSTRONG

Phone: (412) 548-3260
Administration Building
450 E. Market St.
Kittanning, PA 16201
Sondra L. Mervis

BEAVER

Phone: (412) 728-5700 ext.223
Delinquent Property Tax Division
Beaver County Courthouse, 3rd st.
Beaver, PA 15009
Connie Javens

BEDFORD

Phone: (814) 623-4846
206 S. Juliana
Bedford, PA 15522
Paula Sheire

BERKS

Phone: (610) 478-6645
Delinquent Property Tax Division
County Service Center, 2nd Floor
633 Court St.
Reading, PA 19601
Oscar Mogel

BLAIR

Phone: (814) 693-3120
423 Allegheny St.
Hollidaysburg, PA 16648
Fred Foreman

BRADFORD

Phone: (717) 265-1700
Bradford County Courthouse
301 Main St.
Towanda, PA 18848
Nancy Schrader

BUCKS

Phone: (215) 348-6244
Delinquent Property Tax Division
Bucks County Courthouse
55 E. Court St.
Doylestown, PA 18901
William R. Snyder

BUTLER

Phone: (412) 284-5149
Delinquent Property Tax Division
Butler Government Center
P.O. Box 1208
Butler, PA 16003-1208
Joan Chew

CAMBRIA

Phone: (814) 472-1643
Delinquent Property Tax Division
200 S. Center St.
Ebensburg, PA 15931
Ester Donahue

CARBON

Phone: (717) 325-2251
Delinquent Property Tax Division
P.O. Box 247
Jim Thorpe, PA 18229
Joseph Orsulak

CENTRE

Phone: (814) 355-6810
Delinquent Property Tax Division
420 Holmes St.
Bellefonte, PA 16823
Gina Fornicola

CHESTER

Phone: (610) 344-6360
2 N High Street, Suite 120
West Chester, PA 19380
Tracy Macey

CLARION

Phone: (814) 226-4000 ext.2861
Delinquent Property Tax Division
Clarion County Courthouse, Main St.
Clarion, PA 16214
Theresa Snyder

CLEARFIELD

Phone: (814) 765-2641 ext.36
P.O. Box 289
Clearfield, PA 16830
Eugene Tubbs

CLINTON

Phone: (717) 893-4000
Clinton County Courthouse
Water & Jay
 Lock Haven, PA 17745
Patricia A. Edwards

COLUMBIA

Phone: (717) 389-5626
Delinquent Property Tax Division
Columbia County Courthouse Box 380
Bloomsburg, PA 17815
Shirley Drake

CRAWFORD

Phone: (814) 333-7332
Delinquent Property Tax Division
Crawford County Courthouse
Diamond Square
Meadville, PA 16335
Frederick Wagner

CUMBERLAND

Phone: (717) 240-6380
Delinquent Property Tax Division
1 Courthouse Square
Carlisle, PA 17013
John Gross

DELAWARE

Phone: (610) 891-4273
Delinquent Property Tax Division
Delaware County Govt. Center Bldg.
201 W. Front
Media, PA 19063
John Dowd

ELK

Phone: (814) 776-1161
Delinquent Property Tax Division
250 Main St.
P.O. Box 448
Ridgeway, PA 15853
Peggy Schneider

ERIE

Phone: (814) 451-6203
Department of Finance
140 W. 6th
Erie, PA 16501
James Roach

FAYETTE

Phone: (412) 430-1256
Delinquent Property Tax Division
Fayette County Courthouse
61 E. Main St.
Uniontown, PA 15401
Robert F. Danko

FRANKLIN

Phone: (717) 264-4125
Delinquent Property Tax Division
Franklin County Courthouse
157 Lincoln Way East
Chambersburg, PA 17201
Steven Minnick

GREENE

Phone: (412) 852-5225
Delinquent Property Tax Division
93 E. High St.
Waynesburg, PA 15370
Robert Elliott

HUNTINGDON

Phone: (814) 643-3523
Delinquent Property Tax Division
223 Penn St.
Huntington, PA 16652
Richard S. Irvin

INDIANA

Phone: (412) 465-3845
Delinquent Property Tax Division
825 Philadelphia St.
Indiana, PA 15701-3973
Sandra Kirkland

JEFFERSON

Phone: (814) 849-1609
Delinquent Property Tax Division
55 Main St.
Brookville, PA 15825
Paul Corbin

LACKAWANNA

Phone: (717) 963-6731
Delinquent Property Tax Division
200 Adams Ave.
Scranton, PA 18503
Edward Karpovich

LANCASTER

Phone: (717) 299-8222
Delinquent Property Tax Division
50 N. Duke St.
Lancaster, PA 17603
Craig Sahd

LAWRENCE

Phone: (412) 656-2123
Delinquent Property Tax Division
Lawrence County Govt. Courthouse
430 Court St.
New Castle, PA 16101
Gary F. Felasco

LEBANON

Phone: (717) 274-2801
Delinquent Property Tax Division
Municipal Building, Rm. 103
400 S. 8th Street
Lebanon, PA 17042
Diane F. Rhoades

LEIGH

Phone: (610) 820-3119
Tax Claim Bureau
55 Hamilton
Allentown, PA 18105
Larry Kistler

LUZERNE

Phone: (717) 825-1780
Delinquent Property Tax Division
Luzerne County Courthouse
200 N. River St.
Wilkes-Barre, PA 18711
Michael Morreale

LYCOMING

Phone: (717) 327-2248
Delinquent Property Tax Division
48 W. 3rd St.
Williamsport, PA 17701
Irene Migrath

MCKEAN

Phone: (814) 887-5571
Delinquent Property Tax Division
P.O. Box 1535
Smethport, PA 16749
Connie Eaton

MERCER

Phone: (412) 662-3800 ext. 2257
Delinquent Property Tax Division
104 Courthouse
Mercer, PA 16137
Virginia Richardson

MIFFLIN

Phone: (717) 248-8439
Delinquent Property Tax Division
20 N. Wayne St.
Lewistown, PA 17044
Gerald Hepler

MONROE

Phone: (717) 420-3510
Monroe County Courthouse
1 Quaker Plaza, Rm. 103
Stroudsburg, PA 18360
Claudette Segear

MONTGOMERY

Phone: (610) 278-3000
Delinquent Property Tax Division
Montgomery County Courthouse, 8th Fl.
P.O. Box 311
Norristown, PA 19404-0311
Jay Moyer

NORTHAMPTON

Phone: (610) 559-3000
Delinquent Property Tax Division
669 Washington St.
Easton, PA 18042

NORTHUMBERLAND

Phone: (717) 988-4100
Delinquent Property Tax Division
230 A. Market St.
Sunbury, PA 17801
Ronald Scheffler

PERRY

Phone: (717) 582-8984 ext. 25
Delinquent Property Tax Division
P.O. Box 63
New Bloomfield, PA 17068
Margaret Bolton

PHILADELPHIA

Phone: (215) 686-2303
Delinquent Property Tax Division
640 Municipal Services Bldg.
1401 JFK Blvd.
Philadelphia, PA 19102
Thomas Queenan

PIKE

Phone: (717) 296-3441
506 Broad St.
Millford, PA 18337
Robert C. Phillips, Jr.

SNYDER

Phone: (717) 837-4219
P.O. Box 217
Middleburg, PA 17842
Gale A. Jones

SOMERSET

Phone: (814) 445-2071
11 E. Union St., Suite 70
Somerset, PA 15501
Donna Schmitt

TIOGA

Phone: (717) 723-8214
18 Main St.
Wellsboro, PA 16901
Karen Confer

UNION

Phone: (717) 524-8781
Delinquent Property Tax Division
103 S. 2nd St.
Lewisburg, PA 17837
Jean Derr

VENANGO

Phone: (814) 437-6871
Delinquent Property Tax Division
Venango County Courthouse
P.O. Box 708
Franklin, PA 16323
Margaret Spence

WARREN

Phone: (814) 723-7550
Delinquent Property Tax Division
204 4th Ave.
Warren, PA 16365
Bonnie Traywick

WASHINGTON

Phone: (412) 228-6700
Delinquent Property Tax Division
Washington County Courthouse
100 W. Beau St., Rm. 102
Washington, PA 15301
Francis King

WAYNE

Phone: (717) 253-5970
925 Court St.
Honesdale, PA 18431
Bruce Mackle

WESTMORELAND

Phone: (412) 830-3428
Delinquent Property Tax Division
Westmoreland County Cths.
Tax Office
4006 Courthouse Square
Greensburg, PA 15601
erry Wendling

WYOMING

Phone: (717) 836-3200
Delinquent Property Tax Division
1 Courthouse Square
Tunkhannock, PA 18657
Carl Smith, Jr.

YORK

Phone: (717) 771-9603
Delinquent Property Tax Division
1 W. Market Way, 4th Floor
York, PA 17401
David S. Seitz

EMPORIUM

Phone: (814) 486-3348
20 E. 5th St.
Emporium, PA 15834
Staci Stuart

FOREST

Phone: (814) 755-3536
Delinquent Property Tax Division
P.O. Box 421
Tionesta, PA 16353
Pamela Millin

FULTON

Phone: (717) 485-4454
Tax Claim Office
201 N. Second St.
McConnellsburg, PA 17233
Bonnie Keefer

JUNIATA

Phone: (717) 436-7742
Delinquent Property Tax Division
P.O. Box 68
Mifflintown, PA 17059
Paulette Kepner

MONTOUR

Phone: (717) 271-3016
Delinquent Property Tax Division
29 Mill St.
Danville, PA 17821
Luther Cooke

POTTER

Phone: (814) 274-9775
Delinquent Property Tax Division
1 E 2nd St., Rm. 21
Courdersport, PA 16915
Richard McCaigue

SULLIVAN

Phone: (717) 946-7331
Sullivan County Courthouse
P.O. Box 116
Main & Muncy St.
Laporte, PA 18626
Kathy Robbins

Texas

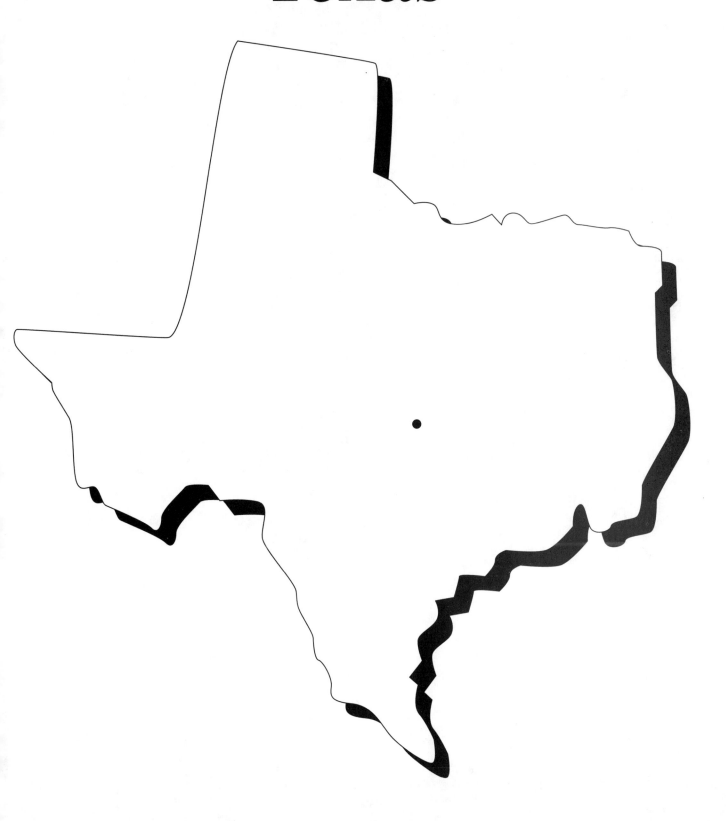

TEXAS

ANDERSON

500 N. Church
Palestine, TX 75802
(903) 723-2949
(903) 723-5990
Cliff Wooten

ANDREWS

600 N. Main
Andrews, TX 79714
(915) 523-9111
(915) 523-3222
Mary Green

ANGELINA

215 E. Lufkin Ave.
Lufkin,TX 75902
(409) 634-8376
(409) 634-2690
Bill Shanklin

ARANSAS

301 Live Oak
Rockport, TX 78382
(512) 729-9733
Jed Smith

ARCHER

40 N. Main
Archer City, TX 76351
(817) 574-2172
(817) 574-4846
Edward Trigg

ARMSTRONG

Trice St.
Claude, TX 79019
(806) 226-4481
(806) 226-2189
Ronald Patterson

ATASCOSA

Circle Drive
Jourdanton, TX 78026
(210)742-3591
(210) 742-3044
Vernon Warren

AUSTIN

1 E. Main
Bellville, TX 77418
(409) 865-9124
Glen Whitehead

BAILEY

300 S. First
Muleshoe, TX 79347
(806) 272-5501
(806) 272-3643
Kay Elliott

BANDERA

500 S. Main
Bandera, TX 78003
(210) 796-3030
(210) 796-3672
Fourth Coates

BASTROP

803 Pine St.
Bastrop, TX 78602
(512) 321-3925
Donna Ripley

BAYLOR

100 Washington St.
Seymour, TX 76380
(817) 888-3169
Grady Hicks

BEE

105 W. Corpus Christi
Beeville, TX 78102
(512) 358-0193

BELL

Central and Main
Belton,TX 76513
(817) 939-5841
Mike Watson

BEXAR

100 Dolorofa
San Antonio, TX 78285
(210) 224-8511
(210) 227-0616
Walter Stoneham

BLANCO

Seventh St.
Johnson City, TX 78636
(210) 868-4013
(210) 868-7330
Hollis Boatright

BORDON

116 E. Bilborn
Gail,TX 79738
(806) 756-4484
(806) 756-4405
R.D. Lewis

BORQUE

100 S. Main
Meridian, TX 76665
(817) 435-2304
(817) 435-6139
Janice Henry

BOWIE

1000 Ninth James Bowie Dr.
New Boston,TX 75570
(903) 793-8936
(903) 792-8889
Wayne Hawkins

BRAZORIA

111 E. Locust
Angleton,TX 77515
(409) 849-7792
Jack Simmons

BRAZOS

300 E. twenty-sixth #314
Bryan,TX 77803
(409) 774-4100
(409) 774-4196
Gerald Winn

BREWSTER

201 West Ave. E.
Alpine, TX 79830
(915) 837-2558
(915) 837-7393
Jerry Ratclif

BRISCOE

415 Main
Silverton, TX 79257
(806) 823-2161
Carlye Fleming

BROOKS

100 W. Miller
Falfurrias, TX 78355
(512) 325-5681
(512) 325-5494
Humberto Rivera

BROWN

200 S. Broadway
Brownwood, TX 76801
(915) 643-5676
(915) 646-8918
Doran Lemke

BURLESON

Buck and Main
Caldwell, TX 77836
(409) 567-4671
(409) 567-7407
Elilzabeth Plagens

BURNETT

220 S. Piece St.
Burnett, TX 78611
(512) 756-8291
(512) 756-7873
Stan Hemphill

CALDWELL

Market and Main
Lockhart, TX 78644
(512) 398-2391

CALHOUN

211 S. Ann
Port Lavaca, TX 77979
(512) 552-8808
(512) 552-4787
Andrew Hahn Jr.

CALLAHAN

400 Market
Baird, TX 79504
(915) 854-1165
(915) 854-1413
Rod Lewellen

CAMERON

954-974 E. Harrison
Browsville, TX 78522
Jessie GarciaCamp
126 Church St.

CAMP

Pittsburg, TX 75686
(903) 856-6538
(903) 856-6544
Vaudaene Bennett

CARSON

500 Main St.
Panhandle, TX 79068
(806) 537-3569
(806) 537-5343
Donita Herber

CASS

101 Rush St.
Linden, TX 75563
(903) 756-7545
(903) 756-3270
Janell Clements

CASTRO

100 E. Bedford
Dimmitt, TX 79027
(806) 647-5131
(806) 647-5132
Jerry Heller

CHAMBERS

404 Washington
Anahuac, TX 77514
(409) 267-3795
(409) 267-6192
Mike Frafregia

CHEROKEE

502 Main
Rusk, TX 75785
(903) 683-5478
(903) 683-2393
Linda Beard

CHILDRESS

100 Avenue E. North West
Childress, TX 79201
(817) 937-6062
(817) 937-3479
Nadine Parr

CLAY

100 North Bridge
Henritta, TX 76365
(817) 538-4311
(817) 538-4725
A.G. Reis

COCHRAN

100 N. Main
Morton, TX 79346
(806) 266-5584
(806) 266-5737
Loy Kern

COKE

13 E. Seventh
Robert Lee, TX 76945
(915) 453-4528
Patsy Dunn

COLEMAN

Commercial Avenue
Coleman, TX 76834
(915) 625-4155
Bill Jones

COLLIN

210 S. McDonald
McKinney, TX 75069
(214) 390-7990
(214) 390-7498
Jimmie Honea

COLLINGSWORTH

802 East Avenue
Wellington, TX 79095
Ann Wauer

COLORADO

400 Spring
Columbus, TX 78934
(409) 732-8222
(402) 732-6485
Billy Youens

COMAL

100 Main Plaza Suite 104
New Braunfels, TX 78130
(210) 625-8597
(210) 625-8598
LynnRogers

COMMANCHE

Court House
Commanche, TX 76442
(915) 356-5253
(915) 356-3650
Clay Fowler

CONCHO

Highway 89 Courthouse
Paint Rock, TX 76866
(915) 732-4389
(915) 732-4234
Jean Dillar

COOKE

Courthouse
Gainsville, TX 76240
(817) 665-7651
(817) 668-2587
Robert Lewis

CORYELL

Seventh And Main
Gatesville, TX 79248
(817) 865-6593
(817) 865-1280
Chief Appraiser

COTTLE

Ninth and Richards
Paducah, TX 79248
(806) 492-3345
(806) 492-3107
Rue Young

CRANE

201 W. Sixth St.
Crane, TX 79731
(915) 558-3713
(915) 558-2520
Peggy Dickson

CROCKETT

907 Avenue D
Osana, TX 76943
(915) 392-2674
(915) 392-2675
Tom Stokes

CROSBY

Aspen and Birkshire
Crosbton, TX 79322
(806) 675-2356
(806) 675-2838
Darla Doss

CULBERSON

300 Lacaverna
Van Horn, TX 79855
(915) 283-2977
Sally Carrascc

DALLAM

101 E. Fifth
Dallahart, TX 79002
(806) 249-6767
(806) 249-4124
Hughie Stanley

DALLAS

501 Main
Dallas, TX 75202
(214) 631-0520
Foy Mitchell

DAWSON

South First and Main
Lamesa, TX 79331
(806) 872-7060
(806) 872-2364
Tom Anderson

DEAF SMITH

235 E. Third St.
Hereford, TX 79045
(806) 364-0625
(806) 364-6875
Fred Fox

DELTA

200 W. Dallas Ave.
Cooper, TX 75432
(903) 395-4118
(903) 395-4455
Troyce Phillips

DENTON

401 W. Hickory
Denton, TX 76202
(817) 566-0904
(817) 387-4824
Joe Rogers

DEWITT

307 N. Gonzales St.
Cuero, TX 77954
(512) 275-5753
(512) 275-9227
John Haiburton

DICKENS

Montgermy Highway 82
Dickens, TX 79229
(806) 623-5216
(806) 623-5319
Jerrie Ballard

DIMMIT

103 N. Fifth
Carrizo Springs, TX 78834
(210) 876-3480
(210) 876-5137
Rufino Lozano

DONLEY

300 S. Sully
Clarendon, TX 79226
(806) 874-2744
(806) 874-5048
Paula Lowrie

DUVAL

500 E. Gravis
San Diego, TX 78384
(512) 279-3305
(512) 279-2622
Ernesto Molina

EASTLAND

100 W. Main
Eastland, TX 76448
(817) 629-8597
(817) 629-2080
Steve Thomas

ECTOR

300 N. Grand
Odessa, TX 79763
(915) 332-6834
(915) 332-1726
James Goodwin

EDWARDS

400 Main St.
Rockspring, TX 78880
(210) 683-4189
(210) 683-6189
Teresa Sweeten

ELLIS

Courthouse
Waxahachic, TX 75165
(214) 938-9807
(214) 937-1618
Richard Rhodes

EL PASO

500 E. San Antonio
El Paso, TX 79901
(915) 544-5530
(915) 544-3743
Cora Viescas

ERATH

Courthouse
Stephenville, TX 76401
(817) 965-7301
(817) 965-5633
Jerry Lee

FALLS

Business Highway 6 and 7
Marlin, TX 76661
(817) 883-2543
(817) 883-3341
Joyce Collier

FANNIN

100 W. Sam Rayburn Dr.
Bonham, TX 75418
(903) 583-9546
(903) 583-4319
Carol LGarrison

FAYETTE

151 N. Washington St.
LaGrange, TX 78945
(409) 968-8383
(409) 968-8385
Kathleen Stewart

FISHER

Highway 180 & 70
Roby, TX 79543
(915) 776-2733
(915) 776-2815
Betty Mize

FLOYD

100 Main
Flotdada, TX 79235
(806) 983-5256
(806) 983-6230
Shelia Faukenberry

FOARD

Courthouse
Crowell, TX 79227
(817) 684-1225
(817) 684-1676
Joann Vecera

FORT BEND

501 Jackson
Richmond, TX 77469
(713) 240-9797
(713) 240-8904
Gene Brewer

FRANKLIN

100 N. Kaufman
Mount Vernon, TX 75457
(903) 537-2286
Ed Marrow

FREESTONE

Commerce St.
Fairfield, TX 75840
(903) 389-5510
(903) 389-5955
Sherrille Minze

FRIO

400 E. Sanitonio St.
Pearsall, TX 78061
(210) 334-4163
(210) 334-5568
Irma Gonzalez

GAINES

101 S. Main
Seminole, TX 79360
(915) 758-3263
(915) 758-3674
Betty Caudle

GALVESTON

722 Mood
Galveston, TX 77550
(409) 935-1980
Ken Wright

GARZA

W. Main Avenue L
Post, TX 79356
(806) 495-3518
Billy Windham

GILLESLPIE

101 W. Main Unit 13
Fredericksburg, TX 78624
(210) 997-9807
(210) 997-9958
Olan Tisdale

GLASSCOCK

Highway 158
Garden City, TX 79739
(915) 354-2361
(915) 354-2661
Royce Pruit

GOLIAD

127 N. Courthouse Square
Goliad, TX 77963
(512) 645-2507
(512) 645-3614
E. J. Bammert

GONZALES

1700 Sarah Dewitt Dr.
Gonzales, TX 78629
(210) 672-2879
(210) 672-8345
Glenda Strackbein

GRAY

200 N. Russell St.
Pampa, TX 79065
(806) 665-0791
Pat Bagley

GRAYSON

100 W. Houston Suite 17
Sherman, TX 75090
(903) 893-9673
(903) 892-3835
Bob Tollison

GREGG

101 E. Methuin
Longview, TX 75606
(903) 759-0015
(903) 759-0967
William Carrol

GRIMES

100 Main St.
Anderson, TX 77830
(409) 873-2163
(409) 873-2499
Bill Sullivan

GUADALUPE

101 E. Court
Sequin, TX 78155
(210) 303-3313
(210) 372-2874
Pat Fox

HALE

500 Broadway # 140
Plainview, TX 79073
(806) 293-4226
(806) 293-1834
Linda Jaynes

HALL

Courthouse
Memphis, TX 79245
(806) 259-3001
(806) 259-3852
Jack Scott

HAMILLTON

Main St.
Hamilton, TX 76531
(817) 386-8945
(817) 386-8947
Doyle Roberts

HANSFORD

1 N. West Court
Spearmount, TX 79081
(806) 659-5575
(806) 659-5109
Alice Peddy

HARDEMAN

300 Main
Quanah, TX 79252
(817) 663-2532
(817) 663-2875
Twila Butler

HARDIN

Highway 326 Courthouse Square
Kountze, TX 77625
(409) 246-2507
(409) 246-4714
Edwin Bery

HARRIS

1001 Preston
Houston, TX 77002
(713) 683-9200
Jim Robinson

HARRISON

200 W. Houston
Marshall, TX 75671
(903) 935-1991
(903) 938-0198
David Whitmire

HARTLEY

9th & Railroad
Channing, TX 79018
(806) 365-4515
(806) 365-4582
Donna Bryant

HASKELL

1 Avenue D
Haskell, TX 79521
(817) 864-3805
Jamie Weaver

HAYS

Courthouse
San Marcos, TX 78666
(512) 268-2522
(512) 268-9245
Bill Cassidy

HEMPHILL

400 Main St.
Canadian, TX 79014
(806) 323-5161
(806) 323-8022
James McCarley

HENDERSON

100 Tyler St.
Athens, TX 75751
(903) 675-9296
(903) 675-4223
Bill Jackson

HIDALGO

100 N. Closner
Edinburg, TX 78540
(210) 781-1545
(210) 702-4634
Daniel Boone

HILL

126 S. Covington
Hillsboro, TX 76645
(817) 582-2508
(817) 582-3654
Shirley Holub

HOCKLEY

800 Houston
Levelland, TX 79336
(806) 894-9654
(806) 894-9671
Nick Williams

HOOD

101 E. Pearl
Granbury, TX 76043
(817) 573-2471
(817) 573-6451
Harold Chestnut

HOPKINS

118 Church St.
Sulphur, TX 75482
(903) 885-2173
(903) 885-2175
Bill Sherman

HOUSTON

401 E. Houston
Crockett, TX 75835
(409) 544-9655
(409) 544-8213
Kathryn Keith

HOWARD

300 Main
Big Spring, TX 75835
(915) 263-8301
(915) 263-8303
Robert Toomire

HUDSPETH

1111 Farm Rd.
Sierra Blanca, TX 74851
(915) 369-4118
(915) 369-2361
John Ferrell

HUNT

2520 Lee
Greenville, TX 75401
(903) 408-4150
(903) 408-4295
Joyce Barrow

HUTCHINSON

500 Main
Stinnett, TX 79083
(806) 274-2294
(806) 273-3400
George Nies

IRION

109 N. Parkview
Mertzon, TX 76941
(915) 835-3551
Frances Grice

JACK

100 Main St.
Jacksboro, TX 76056
(817) 567-6301
(817) 567-3640
Gary Zeitler

JACKSON

115 W. Main St.
Edna, TX 77957
(512) 782-7115
(512) 782-0369
James Surratt

JASPER

P.O.Box 2070
Jasper, TX 75951
(409) 384-2544
(409) 384-7416
David Luther

JEFF DAVIS

Court & Main
Fort Davis, TX 79734
(915) 426-3210
John Farrell

JEFFERSON

1149 Pearl Ave.
Beaumont, TX 77701
(409) 727-4611
(409) 727-5621
Rollin Bieber

JIM HOGG

102 E. Tilley
Hebbronville, TX 78361
(512) 527-4033
(512) 527-5451
Indicate fax is for
Tax Office
Lawson Bolton

JIM WELLS

200 N. Almond
Alice, TX 78332
(512) 668-9656
(512) 668-6423
Joseph Vela

JOHNSON

109 N. Main
Cleburne, TX 76031
(817) 645-3986
(817) 645-3105
Don Gillmore

JONES

12th & Commercial
Anson, TX 79501
(915) 823-2422
(915) 823-2424
Susan Holloway

KARNES

101 N. Panna Maria
Karnes City, TX 78118
(210) 780-2433
(210) 780-4436
Oscar Caballero

KAUFMAN

100 W. Mulberry
Kaufman, TX 75142
(214) 932-6081
(214) 932-4749
Jackie Sell

KENDALL

204 E. San Antonio
Boerne, TX 78006
(210) 249-8012
(210) 249-3975
Mick Mikuleka

KENEDY

101 Mallory
Sarita, TX 78385
(512) 294-5202
(512) 294-5218
Clyde Hamilton

KENT

P.O. Box 9
Jayton, TX 79528
(806) 237-3066
(806) 237-3067
Garth Gregory

KERR

700 Main St.
Kerrville, TX 78028
(210) 895-5223
(210) 895-5227
David Oehler

KIMBLE

501 N. Main
Junction, TX 76849
(915) 446-3717
(915) 446-4361
Paul Bierschwale

KING

Highway 82
Guthrie, TX 79236
(806) 596-4588
(806) 596-4664
Sandy Burkett

KINNEY

501 Ann St.
Brackettville, TX 78832
(210) 563-2323
(210) 563-9495
Markus Tidwell

KLEBERG

700 E. Kleberg
Kingsville, TX 78364
(512) 595-5775
(512) 595-7984
Tina Lorea

KNOX

Highways 6 & 82
Benjamin, TX 79505
(817) 454-2411
(817) 454-2004
Stanton Brown

LAMAR

119 N. Main
Paris, TX 75460
(903) 785-7822
(903) 785-8322
Joe Welch

LAMB

100 Sixth ST.
Littlefield, TX 79339
(806) 385-6474
(806) 385-6944
Vaughn Mc Kee

LAMPASAS

400 S. Live Oak
Lampasas, TX 76550
(512) 556-8058
(512) 556-4660
Tommy Watson

LASALLE

101 Court House Square
Cotulla, TX 78014
(210) 879-2415
(210) 879-3882
Juanita Lozano

LAVACA

201 N. La Grange
Hallettsville, TX 77964
(512) 798-4396
(512) 798-2653
Diane Munson

LEE

Main At Hempstead
Gidding, TX 78942
(409) 542-9618
(409) 542-3705
Roy Holcomb

LEON

Cass & St. Mary
Centerville, TX 75833
(903) 536-2252
(903) 536-2377
Mr. Gillam

LIBERTY

1923 Sam Houston
Liberty, TX 77575
(409) 336-5722
(409) 336-8390
Allan Conner

LIMESTONE

200 W. State St.
Groesbeck, TX 76642
(817) 729-3009
(817) 729-5534
Karen Wietzoski

LIPSCOMB

Main at Court House Square
Lipscomb, TX 79056
(806) 624-2881
Jerry Reynold

LIVE OAK

301 Houston
George West, TX 78022
(512) 449-2641
(512) 449-2771
Robert Dirks

LLANO

801 Ford
Llano, TX 78643
(915) 247-3065
(915) 247-3273
Bill Stewart

LOVING

100 Bell St.
Mentone, TX 79754
(915) 377-2201
(915) 377-2701
J.W. Busby

LUBBOCK

Lubbock, TX 79401
(806) 762-5000
(806) 762-2451
Chief Appraiser

LYNN

Main St.
Tahoka, TX 79373
(806) 998-5477
(806) 998-4057
Dovie Miller

MADISON

101 W. Main
Madisonville, TX 77864
(409) 348-2783
(409) 348-6188
Danny Singletary

MATAGORDA

1700 Seventh St.
Bay City, TX 77414
(409) 244-2031
Vince Maloney

MAVERICK

500 Quarry
Eagle Pass, TX 78854
(210) 773-0255
(210) 773-8652
Victor Perry

MCCULLOCH

Court House Square
Brady, TX 76825
(915) 597-1627
(915) 597-2408
Orlando Rubio

MCLENNAN

Fifth & Washington
Waco, TX 76701
(817) 752-9864
(817) 752-8225
Charles Gauer

MCMULLEN

River & Elm
Tilden, TX 78072
(512) 274-3685
(512) 272-3618
Donald Hanes

MEDINA

1100 Sixteenth St.
Hondo, TX 78861
(210) 741-3035
(210) 426-4660
James Garcia

MENARD

Gay St.
Menard, TX 76654
(915) 4784
Margaret Cannon

MIDLAND

200 W. Wall
Midland, TX 79701
(915) 699-4991
(915) 689-7185
Ron Stegall

MILAM

100 S. Dannin
Cameron, TX 76520
(817) 697-66328
(817) 697-8059
Pat Moraw

MILLS

1011 Fourth St.
Goldthwaite, TX 76844
(915) 648-2253
(915) 648-3458
Cynthia Partin

MITCHELL

301 Oak St.
Colorado City, TX 79512
(915) 728-5028
Kaye Cornutt

MONTAGUE

312 Rush St.
Montague, TX 76251
(817) 894-6011
(817) 894-6599
Wanda Russell

MONTOGOMERY

300 N. Main
Conroe, TX 77305
(409) 756-3354
(409) 539-8695
Jimmy Foreman

MOORE

715 S. Dumas
Dumas, TX 79029
(806) 935-4193
(806) 935-6275
Joyce Cearley

Morris

500 Broadnax St.
Daingerfield, TX 75638
(903) 645-5601
(903) 645-2694
Rhonda Hall

MOTLEY

Main & Dundee
Matador, TX 79224
(806) 347-2273
Brenda Osborn

NACOGDOCHES

101 W. Main
Nacogdoches, TX 75961
(409) 560-3447
(409) 560-1894
Gary Woods

NAVARRO

300 W. Third ST.
Corsicana, TX 75110
(903) 872-6161
(903) 874-0604
Harry Hudson

NEWTON

Loop 501 & Highway 19
Newton, TX 75966
(409) 379-3710
(409) 379-4020
Margie Herrin

NOLAN

100 E. Third St.
Sweetwater, TX 79556
(915) 235-8421
(915) 235-8165
Patricia Davis

NUECES

901 Leopard
Corpus Christi, TX 78401
(512) 881-9978
(512) 887-6138
George Moss

OCHILTREE

511 S. Main
Perryton, TX 79070
(806) 435-9623
(806) 435-4198
Terry Symons

OLDHAM

U.S. 385 & Main
Vega, TX 79092
(806) 267-2442
(806) 267-2471
Jen Carter

ORANGE

801 Division
Orange, TX 77630
(409) 745-4777
(409) 745-4112
Pat Sanderson

PALO PINTO

Highway 180
Palo Pinto, TX 76072
(817) 659-1281
(817) 659-2618
Carol Holmes

PANOLA

Room 201
Carthage, TX 75633
(903) 693-2891
(903) 693-8229
John Pepper

PARKER

1112 Sante Fe Dr.
Weatherford, TX 76086
(817) 599-7671
(817) 594-7362
Larry Hammonds

PARMER

401 Third St.
Farwell, TX 79325
(806) 238-1405
(806) 238-1121
Ron Procter

PECOS

103 W. Callahan
Fort Stockton, TX 79735
(915) 336-7587
(915) 336-2665
John Oglesby

POLK

101 Church St.,W.
Livingston, TX 77351
(409) 327-2174
(409) 327-2545
Clyde Arrendell

POTTER

511 S. Taylor
Amarillo, TX 79101
(806) 358-1601
(806) 355-8426
Jim Childers

PRESIDIO

320 N. Highland
Marfa, TX 79843
(915) 729-3431
(915) 729-4722
Irma Salgado

RAINS

100 Quitman
Emory, TX 75440
(903)473-2391
Lou Dele Dowdy

RANDALL

400 Sixteenth St.
Canyon, TX 79015
(806) 358-1601
(806) 355-8426
Jim Childers

REAGAN

Third at Plaza
Big Lake, TX 76932
(915) 884-3275
(915) 884-2149
Bryon Bitner

REAL

Highway 83 at Market
Leakey, TX 78873
(210) 232-6248
(210) 232-6040
Tilly Sanderlin

RED RIVER

400 N. Walnut
Clarksville, TX 75426
(903) 427-4181
(903) 427-5510
Betty Parke

REEVES

P.O.Box 867
Pecos, TX 79772
(915) 445-5122
(915) 445-5108
Carol Markham

REFUGIO

808 Commerce
Refugio, TX 78377
(512) 526-5994
(512) 526-5994
Betty Kret

ROBERTS

Highway 60 & Kiowa
Miami, TX 79059
(806) 868-5281
(806) 868-4391
Carol Billingsley

ROBERTSON

Center St.
Franklin, TX 77856
(409) 828-5800
(409) 828-5137
Dan Brewer

ROCKWALL

Cameron Building
Rockwell County Government
Suite 101
Rockwall, TX 75087
(214) 771-2034
(214) 771-6871
Ray Helm

RUNNELS

600 Court House Square
Ballinger, TX 76821
(915) 365-3583
(915) 365-5563
Gene Stewart

RUSK

115 N. Main
Henderson, TX 75653
(903) 657-3578
(903) 657-9073
Melvin Cooper

SABINE

Oak & Main
Hemphill, TX 75948
(409) 787-2777
(409) 787-4005
Jim Nethery

SAN AUGUSTINE

106 Courthouse
San Augustine, TX 75972
(409) 275-3496
Jamie Doherty

SAN JACINTO

Church St. & Byrd St.
Coldspring, TX 77331
(409) 653-4481
Mack Ridley

SAN PATRICO

400 W. Sinton St.
Sinton, TX 78387
(512) 364-5402
(512) 364-1198
Kathryn Verlillion

SAN SABA

500 E. Wallace
San Saba, TX 76877
(915) 372-5031
(915) 372-3325
Dave Davenport

SCHLEICHER

Courthouse Square
Highway 277
Eldorado, TX 76936
(915) 853-2617
(915) 853-2603
Ray Vallew

SCURRY

1806 Twenty-fifth St.
Suite 300
Snyder, TX 79549
(915) 573-8549
(915) 573-8458
Ray Peveler

SHACKELFORD

200 Main
Albany, TX 76430
(915) 762-2207
(915) 762-2208
Bruce Bailey

SHELBY

200 San Augustine
Center, TX 75935
(409) 598-6171
(409) 598-7096
Harold Robertson

SHERMAN

701 N. Third
Stratford, TX 79084
(806) 396-5566
(806) 396-2565
Thresa Edmond

SMITH

100 N. Broadway
Tyler, TX 75710
(903) 510-8600
(903) 510-8621
Michael Barnett

SOMERVELL

100 Banard
Glen Rose, TX 76043
(817) 897-4094
(817) 897-2358
Sandra Montgomery

STARR

Room 201
Britton Ave.
Rio Grande City, TX 78582
(210) 487-5613
(210) 487-8555
Jamie Trevino

STEPHENS

200 W. Walker
Breckenridge, TX 76024
(817) 559-8233
(817) 559-7322
Troy Sloan

STERLING

610 Fourth St.
Sterling City, TX 76951
(915) 378-7711
(915) 378-2266
Linda Low

STONEWALL

510 S. Broadway
Aspermont, TX 79502
(817) 989-3363
(817) 989-3566
Stacey Meador

SUTTON

Courthouse Square
Sonora, TX 76950
(915) 387-2809
Rex Friess

SWISHER

Maxwell & Broadway
Tulia, TX 79088
(806) 995-4118
(806) 995-4079
Roselee Powell

TARRANT

100 W. Weatherford
Fortworth, TX 76196
(817) 595-6001
(817) 595-6198
John Marshall

TAYLOR

300 Oak St.
Abilene, TX 79608
(915) 676-9381
(915) 676-7877
Richard Petree

TERRELL

108 Hackbery
Sanderson, TX 79848
(915) 345-2251
Blain Chriesman

TERRY

500 W. Main
Brownfield, TX 79316
(806) 637-2151
(806) 637-4675
Ronnie Burran

THROCKMORTON

105 N. Minter
Trockmorton, TX 76083
.(817) 849-5691
(817) 849-5692
Ruby Dunlap

TITUS

100 W. First
Mount Pleasant, TX 75455
(903) 572-7939
(903) 572-5147
Lois McKibben

TOM GREEN

112 W. Beauregard
San Angelo, TX 76903
(915) 658-5575
(915) 657-8197
Elvin Field

TRAVIS

1000 Guadalupe
Austin, TX 78701
(512) 834-9138
(512) 835-5371
Art Cory

TRINITY

First St.
Groveton, TX 75845
(409) 642-1208
Allen McKinley

TYLER

100 Courthouse
Woodville, TX 75979
(409) 283-3736
(409) 283-8439
Travis Chalmers

UPSHUR

Highway 54
Gilmer, TX 75644
(903) 843-3041
(903) 843-5764
Louise Stracener

UPTON

205 E. Tenth
Rankin, TX 79778
(915) 652-3221
(915) 652-3372
Jo Beth Wright

UVALDE

Main & Getty
Uvalde, TX 78802
(210) 278-1106
(210) 278-8150
Brownie Jones

VAL VERDE

400 Pecan
Del Rio, TX 78841
(210) 774-4602
PaulBillano

VAN ZANDT

121 Dallas St.
Room 202
Canton, TX 75103
(903) 567-6171
(903) 567-6600
Ron Groom

VICTORIA

115 N. Bridge
Victoria, TX 77901
(512) 576-3621
(512) 578-1663
Marvin Hahn

WALKER

1100 University
Huntsville, TX 77340
(409) 295-0402
(409) 295-3061
Grover Cook

WALLER

836 Austin St.
lHempstead, TX 77445
(713) 391-3188
(713) 391-1481
David Piwonka

WARD

400 S. Allen
Monahams, TX 79756
(915) 943-3224
(915) 943-3226
Arlice Whittie

WASHINGTON

100 E. Main
Brenham, TX 77833
(409) 277-6528
(409) 277-6515
Charles Gaskamp

WEBB

204 Mc Pherson Dr.
Laredo, TX 78041
(210) 718-4091
(210) 718-4052
Leta Schlinke

WHARTON

100 E. Milam
Wharton, TX 77488
(409) 532-8931
(409) 532-5691
Larry Holub

WHEELER

100 S. Main
Wheeler, TX 79096
(806) 826-5900
(806) 826-5960
Larry Schoenhalf

WICHITA

900 Seventh St.
Wichita Fall, TX 76307
(817) 322-2435
Lanier Wilson

WILBARGER

1700 Wilbarger St.
Vernon, TX 76384
(817) 553-1857
(817) 552-9541
Doyle Graham

WILLACY

540 W. Hidalgo
Raymondville, TX 78580
(512) 689-5979
Augustine Colchado

WILLIAMSON

P.O.Box 18
Georgetown, TX 78627
(512) 930-3787
(512) 869-2565
Donna Moss

WILSON

1420 Third St.
Floresville, TX 78114
(210) 393-3065
(210) 393-7755
Louis Wall

WINKLER

100 E. Winkler
Kermit, TX 79745
(915) 586-2832
Helen Oldham

WISE

101 1/2 N. Trinity
Decatur, TX 76234
(817) 627-3081
Mickey Hand

WOOD

1 Main St.
Quitman, TX 75783
(903) 763-4946
(903) 763-4183
Carson Wages

YOAKUM

10th & Avenue G
Plains, TX 79355
(806) 456-7101
(806) 456-7102
Sandra Stevens

YOUNG

516 Fourth St.
Graham, TX 76046
(817) 549-2392
(817) 549-7271
Pat Butler

ZAPATA

Seventh Ave.
Zapata, TX 78076
(210) 765-9974
(210) 765-9991
Rosalva Dominguez

ZAVALA

First & Uualud
Crystal City, TX 78839
(210) 374-3475
(210) 374-3076
Richard Diaz

Utah

UTAH

Number of Counties: 30

BOX

Phone: (801) 734-2031
Delinquent Property Tax Division
1 S. Main
Bringham City, UT 84302
Monte Munns

CACHE

Phone: (801) 752-3414
Delinquent Property Tax Division
179 N. Main
Logan, UT 84321
Karen Jeppesen

DAVIS

Phone: (801) 451-3243
P.O. Box 618
Farmington, UT 84025
Mark Altom

SALT LAKE

Phone: (801) 468-3387
Delinquent Property Tax Division
2001 S. State St., N1200
Salt Lake City, UT 84190
Larry Richardson

TOOELE

Phone: (801) 882-9150
Delinquent Property Tax Division
47 S. Main
Looele, UT 84074
Valerie Lee

UINTAH

Phone: (801) 781-0770
Delinquent Property Tax Division
147 E. Main
Vernal, UT 84078
Donna Richens

UTAH

Phone: (801) 370-8255
Delinquent Property Tax Division
100 E. Center
Provo, UT 84606
Leonard Ellis

WASHINGTON

Phone: (801) 634-5711
197 E. Tabernacle
St. George, UT 84770
Alis M. Ritz

WEBER

Phone: (801) 399-8011
Delinquent Property Tax Division
Weber County Treasurer
2549 Washington Blvd.
Ogden, UT 84401

BEAVER

Phone: (801) 438-6463
Delinquent Property Tax Division
Beaver County Treasurer
Beaver County Courthouse
Beaver, UT 84713

CARBON

Phone: (801) 637-4700
Delinquent Property Tax Division
120 E. Main
Price, UT 84501
Marilyn Graham

DAGGETT

Phone: (801) 784-3154
Delinquent Property Tax Division
P.O. Box 219
Manila, UT 84046
Vicki McKee

DUCHESNE

Phone: (801) 738-2435
Delinquent Property Tax Division
P.O. Box 989
Duchesne, UT 84021
Coleen Nelson

EMERY

Phone: (801) 381-2510
Delinquent Property Tax Division
P.O. Box 595
Castle Dale, UT 84528
Joanne Behling

GARFIELD

Phone: (801) 676-8826
Delinquent Property Tax Division
P.O. Box 77
Panguitch, UT 84759
Judy Henry

GRAND

Phone: (801) 259-1321
Delinquent Property Tax Division
125 E. Center
Moab, UT 84532
Grace Easton

IRON

Phone: (801) 477-3375
Delinquent Property Tax Division
P.O. Box 369
Parowan, UT 84761
Myrna Mitchell

JUAB

Phone: (801) 623-0271
Delinquent Property Tax Division
160 N Main
Nephi, UT 84648
Joyce Pay

KANE

Phone: (801) 644-2458
Delinquent Property Tax Division
76 N. Main
Kanab, UT 84741
Marie Mousaw

MILLARD

Phone: (801) 743-5322
Delinquent Property Tax Division
P.O. Box 226
Fillmore, UT 84631
Mary Day

MORGAN

Phone: (801) 829-6811
Delinquent Property Tax Division
P.O. Box 420
Morgan, UT 84050
Gloria Anderson

PIUTE

Phone: (801) 577-2505
Delinquent Property Tax Division
P.O. Box 99
Junction, UT 84740

RICH

Phone: (801) 793-2415
Delinquent Property Tax Division
Box 186
Randolph, UT 84064
Ruth Smith

SAN JUAN

Phone: (801) 587-3237
Delinquent Property Tax Division
P.O. Box 817
Monticello, UT 84535
Paul Barr

SANPETE

Phone: (801) 835-2131
Delinquent Property Tax Division
160 N. Main
Manti, UT 84642
Earl Clark

SEVIER

Phone: (801) 896-9262
Delinquent Property Tax Division
250 N. Main, Rm. 106
Richfield, UT 84701
Leda Johnson

SUMMIT

Phone: (801) 336-4451
Delinquent Property Tax Division
P.O. Box 128
Coalville, UT 84017
Glen Thompson

UINTAH

Phone: (801) 781-0770
Delinquent Property Tax Division
147 E. Main
Vernal, UT 84078
Donna Richens
WASATCH

Phone: (801) 654-3211
25 N. Main
Heber City, UT 84032
Carolyn Kirkham

WAYNE

Phone: (801) 836-2765
Delinquent Property Tax Division
P.O. Box 187
Loa, UT 84747
Loma Blackburn

Virginia

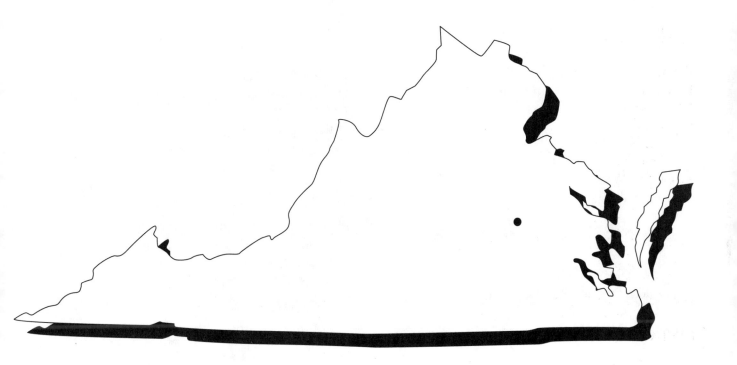

VIRGINIA

Number of Counties: 93

ACCOMACK

Phone: (804) 787-5700
Delinquent Property Tax Division
P.O. Box 296
Accomac, VA 23301
Donna Bundick

ALBEMARLE

Phone: (804) 296-5851
Delinquent Property Tax Division
401 McIntire Rd.
Charlottesville, VA 22902

AMHERST

Phone: (804) 946-9318
P.O. Box 449
Amherst, VA 24521
Donald T. Wood

ARLINGTON

Phone: (703) 358-3120
Delinquent Property Tax Division
2100 Clarendon Blvd.
Arlington, VA 22216
Francis X. O'Leary

AUGUSTA

Phone: (540) 245-5600
Delinquent Property Tax Division
P.O. Box 590
Verona, VA 24482-0590
Alan Maddox

BEDFORD

Phone: (540) 586-7601
P.O. Box 864
Bedford, VA 24523
Norma M. Edwards

BUCHANAN

Phone: (540) 935-6500
Delinquent Property Tax Division
P.O. Box 256
Grundy, VA 24614
Bill King

CAMPBELL

Phone: (804) 847-0961
Delinquent Property Tax Division
P.O. Box 37
Rustburg, VA 24588
Barbara T. Farmer

CARROLL

Phone: (540) 728-9421
Delinquent Property Tax Division
P.O. Box 489
Hillsville, VA 24343
Lois J. McGrady

CHESTERFIELD

Phone: (804) 748-1201
Delinquent Property Tax Division
P.O. Box 70
Chesterfield, VA 23832
Richard Cordle

CULPEPER

Phone: (540) 825-3035
Delinquent Property Tax Division
P.O. Box 1447
Culpeper, VA 22701
Steve Southard

FAIRFAX

Phone: (703) 246-2000
Delinquent Property Tax Division
12000 Government Center Parkway
Suite 223
Fairfax, VA 22035

FAUQUIER

Phone: (540) 347-8600
Delinquent Property Tax Division
P.O. 677
Warrenton, VA 22186
Elizabeth Ledgerton

FRANKLIN

Phone: (540) 483-3078
Delinquent Property Tax Division
102 S. Main
Rocky Mount, VA 24151
Elaine Chitwood

FREDERICK

Phone: (540) 665-5666
Delinquent Property Tax Division
P.O. Box 225
Winchester, VA 22604
C. William Orndoff, Jr.

GLOUCESTER

Phone: (804) 693-2141
Delinquent Property Tax Division
P.O. Box 337
Gloucester, VA 23061
Mary Altemus

HALIFAX

Phone: (804) 476-3318
Delinquent Property Tax Division
P.O. Box 825
Halifax, VA 24558
Linda Foster

HENRICO

Phone: (804) 672-4206
P.O. Box 27032
Richmond, VA 23273
Dennis Kerns

HENRY

Phone: (540) 638-5311
Delinquent Property Tax Division
P.O. Box 218
Collinsville, VA 24078
D.W. Turner

JAMES CITY

Phone: (804) 253-6705
Delinquent Property Tax Division
P.O. Box 8701
Williamsburg, VA 23187
Betty Pettengill

LEE

Phone: (540) 346-7714
Delinquent Property Tax Division
P.O. Box 70
Jonesville, VA 24263
Ikey Joe Chadwell

LOUDOUN

Phone: (703) 478-8418
Delinquent Property Tax Division
P.O. Box 347
Leesburg, VA 22075
H. Roger Zurn

MECKLENBERG

Phone: (804) 738-6191
Delinquent Property Tax Division
P.O. Box 250
Boydton, VA 23917
Robert Gregory

MONTGOMERY

Phone: (540) 382-5723
Delinquent Property Tax Division
P.O. Box 116
Christianburg, VA 24073
Ellis Meredith

PITTSYLVANIA

Phone: (804) 432-2041
Delinquent Property Tax Division
P.O. Box 230
Chatham, VA 24531
Glen Brown

PRINCE GEORGE

Phone: (804) 733-2620
Delinquent Property Tax Division
P.O. Box 156
Prince George, VA 23875
Jean N. Barker

PRINCE WILLIAM

Phone: (703) 792-6730
Delinquent Property Tax Division
1 County Complex Court
Prince William, VA 22192-9201

PULASKI

Phone: (540) 980-7785
Delinquent Property Tax Division
52 W. Main St., Suite 100
Pulaski, VA 24301
Rosemarie Tickle

ROANOKE

Phone: (540) 772-2056
Delinquent Property Tax Division
P.O. Box 21009
Roanoke, VA 24018
Alfred C. Anderson

ROCKINGHAM

Phone: (540) 564-3000
Delinquent Property Tax Division
345 S. Main St.
Harrisonburg, VA 22801
Todd Garber

RUSSELL

Phone: (540) 889-8000
Delinquent Property Tax Division
P.O. Box 121
Lebanon, VA 24266
Helen Baker

SCOTT

Phone: (540) 386-7742
Delinquent Property Tax Division
104 E. Jackson, Suite 8
Gate City, VA 24251
Martha H. Bledsoe

SHENANDOAH

Phone: (540) 459-6180
Delinquent Property Tax Division
P.O. Box 365
Woodstock, VA 22664
Cindy A. George

SMYTH

Phone: (540) 783-5711
Delinquent Property Tax Division
P.O. Drawer 549
Marion, VA 24354
Ruth D. Albert

SPOTSYLVANIA

Phone: (540) 582-7058
P.O. Box 65
Spotsylvania, VA 22553
Larry Pritchett

STAFFORD

Phone: (540) 659-8603
Delinquent Property Tax Division
P.O. Box 68
Statford, VA 22555
Elizabeth Dailey

TAZEWELL

Phone: (540) 988-7541
Delinquent Property Tax Division
P.O. Box 969
Tazewell, VA 24651

WARREN

Phone: (540) 635-2215
P.O. Box 1540
Front Royal, VA 22630
Doris D. Miller

WASHINGTON

Phone: (540) 676-6272
Delinquent Property Tax Division
174 E. Main
Abingdon, VA 24210
Fred W. Parker

WISE

Phone: (540) 328-3666
Delinquent Property Tax Division
P.O. Box 1308
Wise, VA 24293
Rita Holbrook

WYTHE

Phone: (540) 223-6020
Delinquent Property Tax Division
225 S. 4th St.
Wytheville, VA 24382
Sam Crockett

YORK

Phone: (804) 890-3420
Delinquent Property Tax Division
P.O. Box 251
Yorktown, VA 23690-0251
Arlene D. Pollard

ALLEGHANY

Phone: (540) 965-1630
Delinquent Property Tax Division
P.O. Box 240
Covington, VA 24426
Anna Fox

AMELIA

Phone: (804) 561-2145
Delinquent Property Tax Division
P.O. Box 730
Amelia, VA 23002
Pam Conyers

APPOMATTOX

Phone: (804) 352-5200
Delinquent Property Tax Division
P.O. Box 863
Appomattox, VA 24522

BATH

Phone: (540) 839-7256
Delinquent Property Tax Division
Bath County Courthouse
P.O. Box 306
Warm Springs, VA 24484
Mary Blankenship

BLAND

Phone: (540) 688-3741
P.O. Box 145
Bland, VA 24315
Karen W. Harman

BOTETOURT

Phone: (540) 473-8220
Delinquent Property Tax Division
P.O. Box 100
Fincastle, VA 24090
C. Benton Bolton

BRUNSWICK

Phone: (804) 848-3107
Delinquent Property Tax Division
228 N. Main St.
Lawrenceville, VA 23868
Alice C. Maitland

BUCKINGHAM

Phone: (804) 969-4744
Delinquent Property Tax Division
P.O. Box 106
Buckingham, VA 23921
Sandra H. Blanks

CAROLINE

Phone: (804) 633-5380
Delinquent Property Tax Division
P.O. Box 431
Bowling Green, VA 22427
Elizabeth Curnn

CHARLES CITY

Phone: (804) 829-2401
Delinquent Property Tax Division
P.O. Box 38
Charles City, VA 23030
Darlene Giles

CHARLOTTE

Phone: (804) 542-5125
Delinquent Property Tax Division
P.O. Box 267
Charlotte Court House, VA 23923
Madeline C. Boliek

CLARKE

Phone: (540) 955-5100
Delinquent Property Tax Division
P.O. Box 537
Berryville, VA 22611
Linda Coumes

CRAIG

Phone: (540) 864-5641
Delinquent Property Tax Division
P.O. Box 57
New Castle, VA 24127
Sandra Reynolds

CUMBERLAND

Phone: (804) 492-4297
Delinquent Property Tax Division
P.O. Box 28
Cumberland, VA 23040
Lee Pfeiffer

DICKENSON

Phone: (540) 926-1676
Delinquent Property Tax Division
P.O. Box 708
Clintwood, VA 24228
Gary Artrip

DINWIDDIE

Phone: (804) 469-4510
Delinquent Property Tax Division
P.O. Box 178
Dinwiddie, VA 23841
William E. Jones

ESSEX

Phone: (804) 443-4331
Delinquent Property Tax Division
P.O. Box 489
Tappahannock, VA 22560
Frances Ellis

FLOYD

Phone: (540) 745-9300
Delinquent Property Tax Division
100 E. Main Street, Rm. 202
Floyd, VA 24091
Deronda Thomas

FLUVANNA

Phone: (804) 589-8012
Delinquent Property Tax Division
P.O. Box 299
Palmyra, VA 22963
Linda H. Lenherr

GILES

Phone: (540) 921-1240
Delinquent Property Tax Division
130 N. Main St.
Pearlsburg, VA 24134
Richard T. Cook

GOOCHLAND

Phone: (804) 556-5306
Delinquent Property Tax Division
P.O. Box 188
Goochland, VA 23063
Geraldine Parrish

GRAYSON

Phone: (540) 773-2371
Delinquent Property Tax Division
P.O. Box 127
Independence, VA 24348
F.R. Young, Jr.

GREENE

Phone: (804) 985-5214
Delinquent Property Tax Division
P.O. Box 157
Standarsville, VA 22973
Mary Garth

GREENVILLE

Phone: (804) 348-4205
Delinquent Property Tax Division
1750 E. Atlantic St., Rm. 213
Emporia, VA 23847-6584
Rosa D. Doyle

HIGHLAND

Phone: (540) 468-2265
Delinquent Property Tax Division
P.O. Box 512
Monterey, VA 24465
William B. Huffman

ISLE OF WIGHT

Phone: (804) 357-3191
Delinquent Property Tax Division
P.O. Box 79
Isle of Wight, VA 23397
B.H. Perry

KING GEORGE

Phone: (540) 775-2571
Delinquent Property Tax Division
P.O. Box 103
King George, VA 22485
Alice L. Moore

KING WILLIAM

Phone: (804) 769-3011, ext. 4931
Delinquent Property Tax Division
P.O. Box 156
King William, VA 23086
Harry Whitt

LANCASTER

Phone: (804) 462-5630
Delinquent Property Tax Division
P.O. Box 6
Lancaster, VA 22503
Anna Lea Haney

LOUISA

Phone: (540) 967-0401
Delinquent Property Tax Division
P.O. Box 523
Louisa, VA 23093
Harry Lumsden

LUNENBURG

Phone: (804) 696-3354
Delinquent Property Tax Division
P.O. Box 643
Victoria, VA 23974
Betsy Long

MADISON

Phone: (540) 948-6700
Delinquent Property Tax Division
P.O. Box 309
Madison, VA 22727
Corrie M. Smith

MATTHEWS

Phone: (804) 725-2341
Delinquent Property Tax Division
P.O. Box 305
Matthews, VA 23109
Judy Burroughs

MIDDLESEX

Phone: (804) 758-5302
Delinquent Property Tax Division
P.O. Box 182
Saluda, VA 23149
Anita Wilson

NELSON

Phone: (804) 263-4873
Delinquent Property Tax Division
P.O. Box 100
Lovingston, VA 22949
Jim Davis

NEW KENT

Phone: (804) 966-9615
P.O. Box 109
New Kent, VA 23124
Betty Borrell

NORTHAMPTON

Phone: (804) 678-0450
P.O. Box 598
Eastville, VA 23347
E.B. Savage

NORTHUMBERLAND

Phone: (804) 580-5201
Delinquent Property Tax Division
P.O. Box 297
Heatsville, VA 22473
Ellen Booker

NOTTOWAY

Phone: (804) 645-9318
P.O. Box 85
Nottoway, VA 23955
Barbara C. Singer

ORANGE

Phone: (540) 672-2656
Delinquent Property Tax Division
P.O. Box 469
Orange, VA 22960
Phyllis Yancey

PAGE

Phone: (540) 743-3975
Delinquent Property Tax Division
101 S. Court St.
Luray, VA 22835
Gerald Judd

PATRICK

Phone: (540) 694-7257
Delinquent Property Tax Division
P.O. Box 668
Stuart, VA 24171
N. Louise Harris

POWHATAN

Phone: (804) 598-5600
Delinquent Property Tax Division
P.O. Box 87
Powhatan, VA 23139
Louise Reams

PRINCE EDWARDS

Phone: (804) 392-3454
Delinquent Property Tax Division
P.O. Box 522
Pamplin, VA 23958
Farmville, VA 23901
Mable Shanaberger

RAPPAHANNOCK

Phone: (540) 675-3334
Delinquent Property Tax Division
P.O. Box 37
Washington, VA 22747
Francis Foster

RICHMOND

Phone: (804) 333-3415
P.O. Box 400
Warsaw, VA 22572
Edith A. Sanders
ROCKBRIDGE

Phone: (540) 463-2613
Delinquent Property Tax Division
P.O. Box 784
Lexington, VA 24450
Carol Hines

SOUTHAMPTON

Phone: (804) 653-3025
Delinquent Property Tax Division
11272 Ivor Rd.
P.O. Box 250
Courtland, VA 23837
D.K. Britt

SURRY

Phone: (804) 294-5271
Delinquent Property Tax Division
P.O. Box 286
Surry, VA 23883
T.C. Lane

SUSSEX

Phone: (804) 246-5511
Delinquent Property Tax Division
P.O. Box 1399
Sussex, VA 23884
Onnie Woodruff

WESTMORELAND

Phone: (804) 493-0130
Delinquent Property Tax Division
P.O. Box 730
Montross, VA 22520
Earleane Branson

THIS PAGE INTENTIONALLY LEFT BLANK FOR NOTES

RESEARCH

SAMPLE LETTER
Contact the County Government

Name of County _____
State of _____
ATTN : Director, Treasurer, or County Official

Dear Sir/Madam:

I am a private investor, and I'm interested in your annual (Tax Lien) or (Deed) Auction. I am interested and prepared to purchase numerous certificates and to fund these purchases with cash or equivalent at the time of the sale. In order for me to properly prepare for the Auction/Sale, please provide me with the following information:

1. What is the date/time of the next Tax Lien/Deed Sale? _____

2. Where and when will that auction/sale be advertised? _____

3. How often to you advertise sales? _____

4. Is it possible to register by mail? _____

5. What type of payment is required -- cash, cash equivalent, cashier's check and/or personal check? _____

6. What type of bidding process will be used? _____

7. Will the sale be final? _____

8. Will all other liens be cleared from the property as a result of the sale? _____

9. If a foreclosure is necessary, will the county assist in this matter? _____

10. Will I receive a document to verify the purchase? Will it be a deed or a certificate of lien? _____

11. Will you allow purchases via mail? _____

12. When will the list of unsold/unbid-on property be available? _____

13. Is a current list of available property or liens available? If so, please advise the cost, so that I may forward a payment for such list. _____

14. Is a copy of the county and state statutes and rule regarding the Tax Sale available for purchase? _____

Folks, don't expect a quick response, unless you follow up by telephone and fax. Send a LARGE self-addressed, stamped envelope for the information you have requested to be sent to you.

TAX DEED ANALYSIS

1. Where is it located? _____

2. What is the value? _____

3. What is the neighborhood like? _____

4. Is the marketing going up or down? _____

5. What will you do with it? _____

6. Why is a good deal for the prospective purchaser? _____

7. How desirable is the location? _____

8. Is the market appreciating? _____

9. How will you sell it? _____

10. What type of property is it? _____

11. Why do I want this Deed? _____

12. What is the actual cash value? _____

13. Does it have a quick sale value? _____

14. Will it require high maintenance? _____

15. What about the environmental issues? _____

16. What is the upside? _____

17. Can you wholesale it for what you're paying? _____

18. Can you sell it? _____

PURCHASE AND SALE WORKSHEET

CERTIFICATE	DATE BOUGHT	%	TAX	PREMIUM	CHECK#	DATE REDEEMED	REDEMPTION PERIOD	AMOUNT RECEIVED

Specific Details on Tax Deed Purchasing

1. Location: Township, Lot, Block

_____

_____

2. Assessed Value - Year Assessed

_____

_____

3. Bid price (what is the Treasurer asking?)

_____

_____

4. Estimated competition:Low?High?

_____

_____

5. Estimated bid-up price

_____

_____

6. Property indentification or tax number

_____

_____

7. Legal description: Metes & Bounds, or Survey

_____

_____

8. Street Address

_____

_____

9. Type of property:SFR, Raw Land, Office, Commerical

_____

_____

10. Comparable value in neighborhood

_____

_____

11. Appraised value - drive by or from a computer database

_____

_____

12. What will you do with it?

_____

_____

13. Why are you bidding on this property?Resale? Hold?Can't pass up a good deal?

_____

_____

14. Who are you going to sell it to for a profit?

_____

_____

ORDER FORM

Title	Price	Quantity	Total
Guidebook	$ 49.95	_____	$_____
Tax Lien Directory	$ 49.95	_____	$_____
Tax Deed Directory	$ 49.95	_____	$_____
Secrets to Buying Tax Liens &			
Tax Deeds by Mail	$ 49.95	_____	$_____
Quick Start Videos 1 & 2	$ 49.95	_____	$_____
Quick Start Audio	$ 14.95	_____	$_____
30 Secrets Banks & Institutions			
Don't Want You to Know Video	$ 39.95	_____	$_____
Insider's Secrets to Buying			
Tax Liens and Deeds Video	$ 29.95	_____	$_____
1 Year Newsletter Subscription	$ 180.00	_____	$_____
State by State Insiders Video Guide to			
Secured Wealth	$ 399.95	_____	$_____
Shipping and Handling—Please Add	$ 7.95		$_____7.95
		Total:	$_____

THIS PAGE INTENTIONALLY LEFT BLANK FOR NOTES